(Un)usual Stories

Wojciech Salski

W. Salski
Creative Works

ISBN: 978-1-8384997-0-9

DEDICATION

I dedicate this book to my grandparents, who without a doubt are reading
it from the other side.
I hope they appreciate what they see.

CONTENTS

EPIGRAPH

'The meaning of life is to find your gift.
The purpose of life is to give it away.'

~ Picasso

ACKNOWLEDGMENTS

I would like to give thanks to my family, without whom I would not be the person I am today. This book is inspired by years of living in their presence, listening to their wisdom, and experiencing the life I am blessed to have. Thank you for all the advice, support, and love you gave me.

*

I would like to give special thanks to Katarzyna Druszcz, my dear cousin, whose artwork is presented across the pages of this book. It is a privilege to be able to share this creative endeavour with my family. Thank you for being patient with me throughout the process and for your invaluable input in the creation of this book. I am certain this is the beginning of an amazing adventure for the both of us.
May your artwork flourish day by day!

*

Finally, I would like to express my deepest gratitude to all my friends, who over the years offered me their appreciation and helped me to stay up in those moments, where standing was far from easy. It is without a doubt the greatest of life's blessings to have friendships such as ours.

FOREWORD

Have you ever doubted whether any of the stories from your life are worth telling by the bonfire on one of those cold, snowy days of winter getaway…?

I wonder if you did, and most likely I won't get the answer to my question any time soon. Nevertheless, let me confess that I did. A lot. On many occasions in the past, I would think twice before starting a story and even if I did, rarely would I finish without hesitation and taking a few breaks in-between to assert myself that it is worth continuing, looking at my friends and analysing their level of interest and attention. It wasn't helping my storytelling and neither did it help me, as doubt, which so often lingers just on the edge of our awareness, would quickly come up and shake its demotivating face in front of my gaze. *What are you even trying to tell* it would snicker, *there isn't much to it, is there…?* Its voice, only hearable to my mind's ears, would ring the wrong bell a few times, and sporadically take my breath away long enough for the whole story to end. Abruptly. Without a sound. Just like that. And so, it continued through the years, sometimes I would get a hold of it, sometimes it would get a hold of me. Self-doubt versus self-worth, crossing their swords in the endless battle for my souls' sake. I was younger and less committed back then. But it never actually stopped, at some point, I just became too concentrated on my goal to hear the war cries anymore.

*

I appreciate the times when people, who I offer my time, thank me for it in advance. I find it invigorating and pleasant, therefore at this point, I would like to grant you my deepest expression of gratitude. Thank you for letting my words fill your mind at the expense of the precious time of yours. I am truly humbled by your decision to join me on this journey, which you are about to experience.

The stories that you will explore are neither mine, nor anyone else's in the sense of possession. In my belief, life happens to us, each moment of every day, and the choices of ours are only mere expressions of the perspective and willingness ourselves to appreciate, disregard or change their outcomes. It is my wish and hope, that as you read through the pages, you will find things that your heart, mind, and soul desires, and by the end of this journey, you will be a better, more skilful version of yourself. Without a doubt, you have the power to become the person you aspire to be and in that, I would like to be of help. Take what you need, discard what's unnecessary, and most importantly enjoy the process.

*

I wish you all that, which your Self desires. You are already perfect, you are already where you need to be, and you have all that is needed for your dreams to come true. You are yourself the best story anyone could ask for. Unique, exceptional, admirable. So, let the doubt out the back door and embrace yourself. Have a great life.

Sincerely,
Wojciech Salski

BECOMING

'…the past gives you identity and the future holds promise of salvation, of fulfillment in whatever form. Both are illusions.'

~ Eckhart Tolle

PROLOGUE

I don't know if any of us ever actually knows, neither remembers how it is to become alive... Some might say of course it's impossible since you cannot remember anything before your fifth birthday' or 'how could you remember such an early moment of your life anyway'... And I agree. I do not remember it at all. And even if I would say I did, it would be either a one-in-billion phenomenon or just a simple lie. Well, I guess I could be delusional as well, but let's hope I do not fit the profile...

*

It all started in mid-eastern Poland. The year was 1997 and I just joined this joyful playground of earthlings.

I didn't play much at that time. Most of my early days were filled with eating, sleeping, and taking a dump... But let's be honest, whose weren't...?

My childhood was great. I ran around the neighbourhood with my friends, rode my tricycle, argued with my little sister, and eaten a whole a lot of sweets, given to us by our nanny. I liked her.

I cannot remember most of those early years and from what I can remember it was fairly okay, amazing at times, and sometimes a little rough, but whose childhood isn't...?

We are all humans after all...

*

The pen ran out of ink, forcing the boy to stop his writing. He looked around the desk hoping to find a replacement, but with no more than a glance, he realized there is no more. He used them all up. *Classic* he sighed, stood up and marched out the door decisive of finding the means to continue his work. It was an early hour of the morning, just before his 'work from home' was about to begin and time wasn't playing to his advantage. His father was absent, away directing a factory in the south, his mother leaving for work in a moment. Both siblings were still asleep, as he walked down the stairs and entered the kitchen, which fragrant scent of freshly made pancakes brightened his mind and excited the taste buds. *Do you have any pencil I could borrow* he asked his mom, as she was about to leave. *Sorry honey I need to go, check the cupboard by the fridge* she answered hurrying with packing, *there should be some spare ones still... I'll bring you some from work today* she promised, closing the door. The turning of the key with a loud clank underlined the end of the conversation.

The boy checked the cupboards and the drawers, and arriving at the kitchen table, which was already prepared for all three of them and their first meal of the day, he sat down on the chair with resignation, *there goes my writing for today...*

*

A few moments passed as he was sat without moving, seemingly acceptant of his situation, even though the mimics on the face begged to differ. His elbows on the table, he scanned the room with still sleepy eyes, looking for a helping hand. The images on the wall presented his family, three portraits of the kids, two being the group photos of their five, including the parents and their late dog. He pondered gazing at the image, thinking about the difficulties of having a child. *Am I old already if I think of bringing up a kid* he debated, murmuring the question to himself. He gazed at his parents in the photography, looking so young, with him and his sister still in diapers, *how crazy having a child must be...* He heard his thoughts, those of consternation regarding the task of kid upbringing and those that seemed to advertise the idea overall and squinting his eyes in the morning sun that appeared in the window, he recollected his father's opinion on the subject. *It is no easy task* his father once said, *and no one truly knows how to do it...* The boy nodded his head in agreement, realizing he had no clue whatsoever what he would do if his girlfriend would suddenly turn out pregnant. *I think we all just improvise* he remembered his father's commentary. *Wasn't there a quote like this* he struggled to recollect, *something like Shakespeare's all the world's a stage' but a little different...?* His face changed shades, as he tried to remember. After a few unspoken words in an attempt to bring back the memory, he relaxed acceptance of the situation. *Oh well,* he sighed, *at least I know it isn't only me who has to improvise...*

WITH LOVE

What is huge and what is tiny, is a matter of perspective thought the boy, who sat at the dinner table with his family. It was another evening, of what seemed to him 'a never-ending cycle of day and night'.

How much longer until I'm a grown-up he pondered observing his parents talk.

The boy was nine years old, and since the beginning of the year, he was no longer only an older brother. With the arrival of another child, he became the oldest', and this subtle shift provoked a powerful change in the way he recognized his place in the world. The presence of his new-born brother, so small in his view, forced him to reconsider what does it mean to be old. He always thought that he and his sister are small. Now they were no more. Maybe in comparison to his parents, they could still be considered small, but if someone was to measure them alongside the new-born, they would be inevitably announced 'the big ones'. The meal continued as he looked down at the carpet beneath the wooden table and shuffled in his seat. *Still not able to touch the ground* he thought, as he tried pushing his feet closer to the ground, without raising from his seat. The doorbell rang. The parents exchanged looks and his mother left the room. The boy looked up at his father thinking of how life must have been for him before the boy arrived. The father smiled at him and brushed the boys' brownish hair. The front door creaked open, and the boy heard voices of his mother and the guests echoing through the corridors of the mansion. Trying to conclude, who is it going to be, he strained his ears, imagining as strong as he could that his sound antennas aim at the entrance to the room and following the scent of the conversation arrive at the front door. Steps of a few were heard and his mother entered the room, followed by his grandparents. He smiled. *What's up grandpa* he wanted to say but respecting the tables' etiquette he didn't. His grandma approached him and kissed him on the cheek greeting him with sweet words. His nose felt the scent of his grandparent's house and the boy smiled wider, as his memory worked its magic within. His grandfather walked up to the table and shook his fathers' hand. The boy observed the interaction in awe, thinking of how it would be to see from such a height and greet with such strong hands. His grandpa turned to him and raised him out of his seat. *Oh, you are getting heavier my boy* he stated with a smile on his face. The boy was now at the height of the adults, which he extremely enjoyed. He looked at his new-born brother asleep in his little cradle. *I am like a giant now* the boy thought raising himself a little higher, with his hands supported on grandpas' shoulder.

His grandfather kissed him hello and lowered him back to his seat. The boy looked around from his usual, as he thought, perspective, and pondered about the idea of age. *Grandma is older than my mom, but she is smaller* he noticed. *Are people getting smaller when they get old,* he wondered, wishing he could get all the answers right away. His father liked to discuss these thoughts on some occasions, but not at the dinner table and grandpa, who was also sat next to him seemed busy greeting his younger sister. The boy sat respectfully waiting for his turn to speak. His mom explained which plate contains what and what's for dessert. He felt the ball of excitement filling up his stomach, as the dessert was mentioned. The boy looked around the plates, trying to magically find something that did not consist of greens, which he wasn't a fan of, but as the rules of the table stated 'you got to eat your greens'. He chose one of the dishes and scooped the mix of vegetables and rice on his plate. Food spilled onto the plate and created a messy pile, that reminded him of a hill made of trash, like in the cartoons. Momentary thoughts occurred, giving him a subject to consider. *The vegetables are so small* he pondered *but not to the insects they aren't. Maybe for them, they are quite sizeable* he theorized while tamping the rice with his fork. His father placed a piece of steaming hot meat on the boy's plate and encouraged him to eat. The boy nodded promptly and got to eating. *No dinner, no dessert* he remembered, stuffing his mouth with a fork-full of rice.

The dessert was delicious, and the boy still remembered the sweet, creamy taste of the icing when the phone rang. It was sometime past midnight. The boy was asleep with his parents after having a bad dream. He woke up in a panic and, as most of the kids do at those times, ran to their room seeking refuge from the stresses of his childish imagination. *Sometimes it isn't fun to be a kid* he thought in those moments, wishing he could be as brave as his father, and sleep anywhere, anytime. His mother shuffled under the duvet, hugging the boy as his father raised himself to seated and answered the phone supporting the sleepiness with his hand. The boy was awake. He tried to listen to the words on the phone, but they were barely hearable. Facing his fathers' back the boy noticed that his parent tensed. Everything fell silent. The boy didn't know why, but a great deal of anxiety spiked up his upper back, making him shiver briefly. His father did not say anything. His head bowed slightly more, and the boy saw that his father raised one hand to the face. *Who was it* his mother asked quietly, with her eyes still closed. The boy pushed himself to seated and with the move, awaken his mom more. The father was sat still with his hand against his head, they couldn't see his face. The boy felt the heart beating faster than before and hugged his mother in a feeling of worry. His mother repeated the question adding *is everything okay* at the end. But everything was not ok. The boy felt it. His father moved slightly and took a deep breath turning to face them. His face was red and expressed a great deal of trouble. When his parents' eyes met, the boy felt as if the information was already there. His mom tensed, hugging him stronger, and with hesitation took the phone that the father handed over. The boy looked into his fathers' eyes trying to understand what is going on. The father raised his hand and brushed his brownish hair, making up a forced smile. *It's all going to be ok my boy* he whispered with his voice breaking. The boy heard the voice on the phone. *It's about your father* someone said, and as if rehearsed both of the parents broke into cry. The boy felt an overwhelming wave of tears gathering at the back of his eyes and melted into a worrisome state of mind. *Something bad happened* he heard his own voice, which trying to catch up with the emotions asked the obvious. His father closed to him and mom and embraced them. They cried. His mother seemed in panic, her sobbing interrupted with sharp in-breaths and sniffles. The boy was in the middle of it, feeling both of his parents' hearts racing next to his, and thought of the meaning of the words on the phone. *It is something to do with grandpa* his mind concluded, as another rush of sadness filled his chest. He felt lost. Not willing to accept the truth, he wrestled with thoughts reasoning the meaning of it all. *He was going to show me the press on our next visit* the boy murmured to himself, interrupting the waves of tears.

His parents strengthened the embrace, as the door opened. His sister entered the room, trying to comprehend what's happening. The boy thought of some special connection between them all, that made her sense that something was wrong and wake up. His father reached out to her and all four of them sat on the bed in a still embrace. His sister started crying too. *It's okay to cry sometimes* his moms' words echoed through the boys' minds, and once again the rush of tears freed them from their prison. The boy felt the sadness and fear with all his body. It was like the whole world disappeared for a moment under a huge dark blanket of grief. He didn't understand it all yet, it was his first time dealing with such emotions, but deep down inside he felt it, vividly and greatly. His thoughts raced, as memories of his grandparents emerged. The boy knew that there is something like death. He saw it in cartoons and heard about it in the news. One time, when the boy has cut his finger open, his father even told him that an ignored wound could bring death too, but he has never experienced it truly. He knew his grandparents will die someday, he knew that his parents would die someday, he knew that he was to die someday as well, but all these ideas were merely subjects of a conversation, interesting facts, nothing more. For the first time, the boy felt mortal and insignificant. For the first time, he felt his heart pried open and his body distressed in the fearful state. He sobbed, cried, and groaned with sounds, which he had not made ever before, as his soul and body struggled with the process of grief.

*

The sunny morning did not fit the day. The boy was sat at the kitchen table, dressed in a dark suit, and looked out the window, lost in his thoughts. He felt stupid and empty. He felt like days like this one should not exist. His father invited everyone to get into the car. It was time to go. The boy flinched, feeling as if this moment was yet again, a shift in how the world is. *At least in my opinion* he thought, walking down the steps to the car. His 'not so little anymore' hand clasped on a piece of wood - his last present for grandpa. His mom said that it's a great idea when he first proposed it. The boy was carrying a wooden board, which he used to paint his toy figures with when visiting his grandparent's house. The board was now covered in purple paint and included a brief message from the depth of the boys' heart. The boy climbed into the car and sat next to the cradle of his little brother. The baby was asleep, with its tiny hands clasped on one of the fluffy toys. The boy looked at his brother and rested his hand next to that of the new-born. The difference in size was great and the boy once more thought of that handshake that his father and grandpa exchanged that day. He thought of the idea of old, and what does it mean to be big depending on the circumstances and point of view.

The boy thought of his grandpa and of all the times he amazed the boy with his abilities. He thought of the time when his grandfather created wooden dogs for all the children, making them from pieces of the old fence; and of the time when without hesitation his grandpa would chase the ball into the sea before it was too late to get it back; and of the time when he took him to the roof of the summer house and made him feel like a giant, looking down at his family in the garden. The boy thought of all those things and his heart settled a little more. The car left the patio, and the journey began. Everyone was silent, all in their own thoughts, tackling the terms of the reality, as they drove to the funeral.

*

The service started just before teatime and the boy noticed that there are much more people present than he was expecting. The church was full, and assuming that there must be a few ceremonies happening today, considered most of the people inside not a part of 'their' celebration. All his known family was here. His cousins, uncles, and their parents were present, making it the biggest family gathering he has so far experienced. The church felt different, almost surreal, with some of the colourful windows covered in a grey veil. After a few religious sketches that the boy didn't pay much attention to, the guests raised in their seats and slowly made their way through the hall of the building towards one of the side halls. The boy followed his parents without a word, not knowing what the purpose of this commotion is. As they approached a little space between the pillars the boy noticed the stand. A wooden, dark brown coffin was fixed on top of it, in the middle of the space, and each guest, one by one, approached the box for a moment. The boy was not able to see what's inside but the twists in his stomach assumed without hesitation. The boy squeezed his fathers' hand stronger as fear emerged. They approached the stand and his father picked him up to see what the coffin contains. The boy gasped shocked, looking down at the peaceful face of his beloved grandpa. His father encouraged the boy to say goodbye to grandfather, and so the boy did. Thoughts of doubt entered the boys' mind, pushing the idea that it is untrue, and that his grandpa is alive; and so, the boy reached out and put his hand on the strong, big hands he has seen so many times. He flinched as he felt an unusual temperature of the body. His grandfather's hands were cold. The boy considered it to be that which distinguishes life and death, and for the first time felt at peace with the situation. Keeping in mind that dying leads to heaven, as taught by the books and traditions of his family, his heart settled and filled with the warmth of the love that connects those of the realm of living with those on the other side.

The boy touched his grandpas' hand one more time, and his father moved away taking him along. His eyes fixed on the coffin as they were walking away, the boy murmured to himself, thinking that, if what they say is true, his grandpa hears it all right now. The words that echoed through the membranes of his mind, and through the world far greater than that visible, established the way his older self-perceived the man who was his grandfather. *You were the coolest grandpa in the world* the boy whispered and closed his eyes thinking of the last time he saw him.

He was a giant the boy thought remembering the hydraulic press, his grandpa's hands, and the metal that disappeared between the platforms as if there was no problem in squishing iron...

WITH CARE

Sometimes crying seems like the only suitable reaction to the events unfolding within and without our minds...

The boy was sat on the terrace of his family's summer house, listening to the sounds of the night with a pervasive feeling of doom and unhappiness creeping up from all dark corners of the porch. He felt his limbs stiffening, his heartbeat unchangingly racing, his palms clammy and somehow disfigured by the squeezing of the hands, as he appeared to be praying. It wasn't anyone, certain prayer, but a monologue of thoughts, moves, and sounds that his soul seemed to be used to conquer the fears appearing underneath his scalp, and somehow reach reassurance of the person that knows whether all that is happening is just a mere overacting of a little, almost inexistent issue. His phone laid next to him, ready to be of service if the situation would raise this necessity, his gaze soft, sometimes lacking in focus, as his eyes shifted between the conscious and unconscious. He was close to falling asleep, but the racing heart fuelled with fear and worry had known better, making his exhausted body stay on guard, his mind coming up with more and more solutions for each of the arising thoughts. And there were many of them.

*

It all started about an hour earlier when his family was preparing for the midnight rest. He was reading his newly acquired book, which ironically enough, treated about the power of the mind and the influence one has over one's body when out of the blue his brother started feeling sick. Initially treating it with a little doubt, a reserve towards the little one's worries, he tried to calm his sibling down and ultimately let them both enjoy the nights' rest without an issue. But the problem did not subside and over a few moments became much bigger than the boy had ever thought it could. His little brother was getting into a shock, or at least that was what the boy thought of this kind of situation. Having experienced a few situations before and being once a lifeguard for over two years of his career, he quickly recognized the need to calm his fellow down and release the suffering that was arising within the little one. The parents were already present adding to the feel of safety, but in the view of the boy also adding a level of worry as the little boy was becoming more and more self-conscious of his surprisingly high heartbeat and a prevailing feeling of doom, which followed.

13

As his brothers' heart raced, the decision was made to try and take the option of summoning an ambulance, as the situation seemed to be getting out of control. The boy thought it not to be the greatest idea but leaving the decision-making to his carers, he sat down next to his little brother and focused all his attention and power of the mind on calming him down. Placing his hand on the brothers' chest and asking him to do the same, he asked him to feel into his own heartbeat and adjust his rapidly racing heart to the reverberating sounds of his hearts' cannonade. Speaking softly and calmly, he kept the conviction going, making sure his brother focuses on the interaction and takes away a bit of pressure from the mind, which raced, accelerating the train of destructive thought, such as the fear of an upcoming heart attack.

*

The ambulance, along with his parent's car, was gone and the boy was left alone on the porch, with their dog sleeping cosily on his bed inside. Not knowing what is happening and considering an ambulance take-away to be a certain degree of seriousness, he no longer held the firm belief in the triviality of the situation and the state his brother found himself in. *A mind is a powerful tool* he reminded himself, trying to wrestle with the arising negative, full of tragedy and suffering, thoughts, *one needs to understand that the mind does not always speak the truth...* His own heart raced now, as he entered the passcode to his mobile and rested his hands in the lap, letting the recording softly flow through him. He was meditating and praying with the wish to send all the positive and healthy feelings to his brother, who was at that time probably somewhere between the first and the second village away from their summer house. He was motivated to not let this situation worsen and after his mother's commentary, when she was leaving for the door, he felt the need to somehow help alleviate this tragically spiralled situation. *It looks serious* he reminisced her words, *like a heart attack...* The boy was a little annoyed at her for sharing this kind of thought with him, as understanding the power of the mind, he already felt the overwhelming worry considered with this kind of statement but realizing that there was no bad intention behind those words, just a common mother's worry, he was determined to help with this as best as he could. But now he was there on the terrace, left alone with his thoughts in the middle of the night and it was not easy to keep the smiling, happy-go-lucky type of an attitude.

*

His mind was playing worrisome tricks on him, making him come up with more and more rather negative ideas of what can take place in the upcoming hours.

That is why he decided to meditate, pray, and ultimately stay up and help his brother through the medium of the mind, which shining through the Universe, was able to help no matter the physical distance. He shed a tear and went inside, drawing out one of his pieces of paper, on which he was writing all kinds of journal and affirmation type of writings each day. It was time to put this power into work. He laid out the piece of paper and swallowing his tears, he started writing. Affirming the safety, wellbeing, and healthiness of his brother's life, he started crying. Trying to stop the tears from staining the paper, he sobbed. The time was somewhere after one in the night, his dog fast asleep, his brother and parents away from him, his mind playing to his disadvantage. Sobbing filled the space, making him feel the doom, which seemed to be creeping in from all corners of his mind. But he knew the weight of his thoughts, and thanks to the understanding of the mind, he kept his ideas in check. Writing out two pages of reasons for which his brother should be left safe and sound and come back home promptly, he cried. Three quarters down the second page his phone buzzed, the message from his mother appeared on the screen. *It looks okay now* she messaged, *get some rest dear.* The boy broke into a cry, letting his emotions come up and flow out of his mind and soul like a waterfall, which finally was freed from the winter's cold arms. Waves of happiness seemed to wash away the dirt of negative thinking. He finished writing, took the paper, and left it underneath his pillow. He was fast asleep before he knew it.

FOR ALL

What makes us who we are if not the experiences, people, and places we encounter throughout our lives...?

The boy pondered on the number of places he lived to this day. Despite his young age, he had already six different addresses signed to his name at any given time. Changing places of stay didn't bother him too much, *it's a part of the life* he thought. Starting back home, moving with his family to the outskirts of his beloved city, and then after finishing the first major phase of his education he made an effort of traveling abroad, and moving into different houses with different people for almost five years, living and breathing multiple situations and lifestyles. He lived with sports fanatics, peaceful Earth-lovers, foreign human beings as well as, his girlfriend at the time. All of these played a part in forming the life of his. He stood outside his house, sipping coffee, and contemplating the plate stuck on the front wall of the house across the street. *'Here lived... in the years...'* he read the message engraved in the shiny, navy blue metal plate and considered what would make someone stick such memorabilia on one of the houses he has inhabited someday. *Wouldn't that be something* he chuckled, *wonder if they had to include their address in one of their works for this platter to take place... Surely someone must have known that they stayed there through these mentioned years* he thought.

*

He looked at his hands, which didn't change much since he became of age, *too early for that* he concluded, *still have some stuff to do to earn it...* There was a quiet consideration of how many different lives have passed through the flat he moved into recently. Decisive that the number of them must have greatly excelled the amount he could imagine; he went up the stairs and pushed the front door open. The living room brightened with the outside light, reminded him once again, that the place he chose for this year to stay wasn't bad at all. He liked the brightness of the day, which crept into space through the wide street-facing window. He recollected the year of living in the house, which had its living room with barely any natural light available, the lightbulb of synthetic, glimmering light being their source of shine. *I hated that room* he recalled; *not enough light makes it feel very suffocating.* He remembered the number of times when coming back from a long day of work, he would enter the room, which filled with marihuana smoke stank of dirty socks and human sweat, his flatmates stuck to the couches, as if they were planted to grow there and wither with time, *it was quite something...*

His memories flashed through the screen of his mind, making the solitude of the flat he lived in nowadays seem a little sad; he missed those people. *We had some great time together, that's for sure* he concluded, and approaching the fridge, take out a bottle of orange juice. The vivid colour of the liquid, balancing on the edge of yellow and orange, filled the glass, which he took and stepped towards the desk, turning on his writing laptop, *time to create.*

*

He wrote a few lines of appreciation of the people and places he experienced throughout his past few years of studies; his workdays of constant rush from one place to another; his efforts to make his ends meet to leave his parents' money to support the other siblings' wellbeing. *It is a great feeling to not need more from them* he thought, *they did their part, now it's my responsibility to bear and soon enough to give back in tenfold...* He sat upright on his wobbly chair, which provided by the landlord certainly wouldn't pass the safety-at-work test. He chuckled thinking of the prospect of inviting such officials over to experience for themselves the quality of seating this piece of furniture offered, *they wouldn't be too happy about it* he pondered. The lines of words squeezed into sentences filled the screen, as he wrote away his thoughts and emotions, letting his palms dance across the keyboard under the creative spell. In awe of the process, it took to write a new, different piece of thought, he recognized how the work of a writer did not vary much from its industry ancestors. *Always slightly bent over a piece of paper, typewriter, or laptop* he thought, *always slamming away tangles of letters and signs, which in the end brought the beauty out of anything the creator desired to touch upon...* He loved it. His passion grew with each day, as he pursued the career he so longed for since he could remember. His mom always claimed that he was the most outspoken child of all in their family, constantly chatting away, making up stories, and bringing to life ideas, which sometimes completely out of order boiled in his mind on a high-temperature hob. There was something special in writing and he knew it. It gave a chance to express one's thoughts without the need to speak and freestyle, trying to keep the interest of the conversation partner before such would evaporate. *I wonder what my friends are up to these days* he stopped, looking outside the wide window towards the far corners of the Earth, where all of them have moved, *I will see them again for sure...*

His alarm beeped, announcing the time to stop his passion work and leave to enter the land of the work that paid for his bills.

*

Just for now, he reminded himself, giving expression to his will to one day being able to pay away his life's expenses with what writing could bring him, *for now, I got to go...* He finished the paragraph, saved his progress, and catalogued it into the folder filled with random thoughtful pieces of his. He didn't even remember most of them, which created in the early hours of the day gave expression to his perspective on life and its many values. He picked up his office card, the bag with his work laptop, and the coat in case it would rain again, and left the flat for another few hours of daily money-making. Walking through the streets so familiar to his feet after many years spent in its space, he thought of all the plans and wishes that one day sooner or later would certainly become true. *I am here because of how I did in the past, thanks to all of you who I've met, thanks to all the houses and situations I experienced* he pondered; *therefore, it is only fair to give back to the world in the best way I can.* He thought for a moment, crossing the road. *That is through writing, I believe,* he concluded and smiling to the sun, which for a moment flashed its beams upon his face, he walked towards the office.

ORIGINAL MANIACS

Considering each one of us sees the world through their own, personal, subjective lens we are all, more or less, 'lunatics of our own design'...

The boy discussed the matter of creating art with his close friend while reading out his poetry. He shared his works, laughing here and there as the memories of the states that drew the words out on the page emerged. *It's weird how much I write and not remember at all* he pointed out, realizing that yet again the piece that he is reading out does not ring a bell, *almost as if I was a little crazy...* They both laughed at the remark and flipping through the pages of his notebook, they considered the idea of creative state separate from that of a conscious mind. *Sometimes I feel like writing happens and I am merely a witness to it* the boy added *like it's coming from out there,* he waved his palm above his head and smiled in a goofy manner. *You might be mad* his friend smirked, shaking her head in disbelief, *how come you don't remember your work...?* He looked at her, frowning his eyebrows a little and letting the words spill out as they wish expressing his thoughts *'we are all lunatics of our own design'.* The girl laughed briefly, accompanied by his chuckle, and they both looked at the page covered with randomly grouped words, that somewhat surprisingly made sense altogether and looked as if their place was exactly where they were set. *Poetry is difficult* the girl pointed out; *I don't think I can do it...* The boy moved his finger across the lines on the paper and conjured his thoughts, making sure that what he was about to say didn't sound too arrogant. *I think anyone can write, poetry or not* he started, *writing well takes time and practice, but ultimately this is such a subjective work that there isn't any bad one... It's just that some poems are more commonly appreciated than others, which kind of makes them the 'better ones'* he mimicked the sign of inverted commas with his hands and smiled, *but I think it's just a matter of letting your hand wander across the page the way it feels like... Like letting it do its magic...*

*

His friend asked for the interpretation of one of the poems, which seemed a little difficult to understand straightforwardly. He looked at the piece and realizing quickly that he doesn't remember writing it either, he shrugged his arms with a confused look written on his face, *I don't know if I can interpret it...* The girl laughed briefly, thinking it was a joke but quickly stopped herself as she realized what he meant, *you can't interpret your own work!?* She couldn't believe it. He shook his head smiling apologetically, *it's not that easy to explain poetry sometimes...*

It's more of an expression than an actual work with substance, theme, and contemporary bits... His friend laughed a little and touching the page above the title of one of the poems, she looked at him *try to interpret this one then, like back in school...* The boy smiled weirdly, remembering crucifying hours spent bent over the pieces of writing made by some other 'lunatic' couple centuries before him, trying to explain the reason why that particular individual decided to shorten the sentence by taking away the word 'the', and instead pushed it into the line below confusing the hell out of anyone who was to read his poem; even more so, confusing those, who were unlucky enough to be interpreting it. He squeezed his hand in a fist for the memory of his awful, always shouty language teacher from high school, who wanted with all her heart to keep him away from attempting A-Levels, which boiled his blood whenever he reminded himself of those times of his adolescence. *Okay* he nodded; *I'll give it a try...*

*

Their evening spent on digesting the words, which that intuition and creative flow of the boy's work spilled over the pages of the notebook, they laughed a lot. Trying to interpret your writing might as well be quite tricky, as the boy soon discovered. They talked about the past experiences at school; the idea of a creative 'zone', which the boy felt more and more often these days, and how peculiar it is to not be able to recognize your own work, even though you might have created it no more than a few days before. He enjoyed his time spent that night with his friend interested in his artwork. He considered himself to be an artist in progress, getting better with each word and line laid out on the page. Falling asleep later that night, he recalled the funny sentence that he came up with while defending his weird lack of knowledge of his craft, *we are all a little mad* he concluded, *like subjectively looking lunatics of our own design...* Laughter bade farewell to the day, as the boy turned off the light and fell asleep soon after.

OUT THERE

There is only one person each of us should strive to impress and compete with every day. It is each of us, for ourselves...

The boy finished reading and putting the book back on the shelf he leaned towards his phone screen, anticipating the line of notifications ready to be encountered. The glassy surface lit up and the screen emerged, showing nothing but the hour of the day and its date. *Weird* the boy thought, *usually, at this point, there is at least one notification...* Approaching the kettle, ready to get the morning routine started, he realized the thought process that has just taken place within his mind a moment ago. He wanted that notification, his ego wanted it. Drawing a conclusion from this situation, he poured himself a cup of coffee and sat down in front of his notebook. *We look for appreciation from others* he scribbled, *without searching for an appraisal from ourselves...* Scratching his unshaven chin, he pondered on the idea. *Seems as absurd as the book described it,* he murmured, and shuffling in his seat, he reached for the book to double-check one of the sentences. *If you will be doing only what others think you should, you would end up living someone else's life...* He read the statement again and leaning back in his seat, he allowed his mind to digest this little dose of medicine for the soul. *If you care more for what others think of you, rather than what you think of yourself* his thoughts arranged themselves in a row, making it to a phrase-like order, *you are never fully satisfied, as their ideas are theirs and there is no way to know what it is they are thinking anyhow...*

*

He sat in silence with a little grin of disgust lingering on his face. Thinking of all the times, when driven by the need to be, do or have exactly what the world 'out there' provoked him to wish for, he realized just how much of his life is influenced by the external audience. *It's like a theatre play, in which each phrase and act needs to be applauded by the spectators, otherwise being discarded and scrapped in the next performance* he concluded, *that would be madness, wouldn't it...?* Feeling the waves of chuckle mixed with a sour taste of salty objections towards his actions, the boy left the book on the shelf and sunk deeper into the chair, letting his hands rest gently on his chest. *So shameful* he heard himself whisper, *so shameful...* Remembering the concept of psychological state called the 'imposter syndrome' he thought of the absurdity of the idea that by being the way others wish us to be, we are supposedly better off than being ourselves.

Isn't it the greatest expression of the imposter syndrome he announced, sarcasm screaming down the well of his mind, *isn't this the most shameful act one can commit…?* Visibly irritated with the repulsion he felt for himself, seeing on the screen of his consciousness all the previous situations, in which his wish to 'fit in' took his freedom of self away replayed endlessly over and over again, he squeezed his palms into fists, and noticing the arising annoyance allowed the feeling to wash over and cleanse itself. *Good that I see it now at least* he hissed through his clenched teeth.

*

Pondering on all the situations that could have gone differently if his actions would not be influenced by the fear of disagreements from his parents, friends, or peers, the boy tried to come to terms with his discovery. *I did the best I could in the circumstances* he reminded himself, *that is essentially what each of us does, constantly… The only trick and issue being, we seldom know whether what we think is best, actually is best to be done in such a situation…* His morale boosted a little as he allowed a small amount of acceptance and understanding for his own mistakes of the past, he picked up his pen and wrote another sentence underneath the first one. *Take into account the opinions of others only if the decision you are about to make, involves them explicitly and has an immediate effect on their life.* He looked at the phrase, thinking whether this he has managed to tackle the idea of 'doing the right thing'. *But even if that would be the case, make sure to put your aspirations first, do not hurt anyone but do not let anyone stop you from doing what is true to your heart* he added, underlining the sentence, and sighing deeply, as a wave of relief flushed down his spine. *Be your own hero and your own greatest contender* the boy recited, standing up and taking his day head-on, *just be yourself.*

OVERCOMING

'Strength and growth come only through continuous effort and struggle.'

~ Napoleon Hill

MAKE YOUR BED

If you want to change the world, start the day by making your bed…

The boy was sat in his parent's garden, sipping his morning coffee, and attentively engaging with his daily chores wrote down a sentence, which at the time when he first heard it, made his heart skip a beat. Something so simple, yet so meaningful, became his rule to live by, whenever there was anything in his life worth achieving or changing. He pondered on the words of the old army general, who in his speech[1] to one of graduating students acknowledged the importance of getting things done in a consecutive, persistent, and humble manner. The boy felt the power drawn from the wisdom presented. It just felt right to him. Since he heard this idea a few years later, he has successfully transformed certain aspects of his life and grew more confident in the belief that this approach does bring effects and works with whatever one must do. Of course, he was still struggling to make the bed each day… *But that's not what he solely meant* he recognized each time he would come back to an unmade bed in the evening, after a day's work, *it's all about doing things as they should be done again and again. To acknowledge that power lies in persistence and discipline* he concluded.

*

His last years passed with him graduating from university, finding, and losing a few jobs, falling in love, and falling out of it, experiencing both good and bad of which the Universe had on the menu for him. Nevertheless, he had not felt bad about it all. Regardless of the many setbacks, hardships, shortcomings, and times when it all felt pointless, the boy has gained plenty of experience, and slowly but surely progressed through this journey called 'life'. His approach adapted, his mind settled with some of the thoughts, and thanks to his overwhelming drive to achieve, exceed and improve, he has managed to conquer many of his previous flaws and fears. The approach proposed by that general and his speech was one of great power and influence in the boy's life. One could argue that through a commitment to abide by the rules offered by the soldier, the boy has literally transformed himself. And seeing the results, he has grown more confident and decisive about the radical legitimacy of the presented approach.

---

[1] W. McRaven. *Make Your Bed: Little Things That Can Change Your Life… And Maybe The World*, 1st Edition, New York: Grand Central Publishing, 2017

His belief in discipline, persistence, and constant progress, even if the pace of the progression was next to none, gave him tools to change multiple things that might have bothered him in his life before this process of consistent advancement. He took another sip of his morning drink and laid palms of his hand on the keyboard, letting them write out yet another text to add to his portfolio. He did it almost manually as if it wasn't him writing the sentences anymore. Thinking of all the beautiful changes he has experienced in his life following the general's approach, he decided to list them all in the name of inspiration to those, who would someday read his testimony. Feeling the flame within himself burning stronger, as he connected with his legend, he noted down a few bullet points, deciding to elaborate on them once the list felt exhausted. *Learning a new language through a simple, fifteen minutes a day app; bringing my body to the fittest shape I've ever been; calming my mind completely with a ten-minute-a-day meditation practice* he mumbled to himself, as his palms noted down each achievement of his, *reading over twenty books during a year; learning how to write creatively and bringing myself to create over fifty different short stories and counting...* His list didn't seem exhaustive but had a certain satisfying feel to it. He felt complete with each of the things the list presented. He felt at home. Recognizing the power of small but steady growth, which presented by the general could be enclosed in the sentence *if you want to change the world, start the day by making your bed,* was the most powerful of all motivational and philosophical approaches the boy has encountered so far. Seeing the results unfolding in his life, he knew that there was strong, transformative energy within this simple mindset of getting one task completed, whatever the significance and size of it were. One small task at a time. He knew that there is much more to be done and that these are only the beginnings of what he could achieve in his life, but recognizing this tactic early on, he felt energized and prone to acquire and succeed more and more each day.

*

Because the growth, however insignificant at the moment, will someday be looked back at and recognized as a huge pile of completed little steps, that in the end became a huge jump the boy thought, *which at the time could have seemed impossible due to its size and radicality. No one has climbed Mount Everest in one go after all...*

CREATE GOOD HABITS

Apparently, by the time we reach the age of thirty-five, 95% of our behaviour consists of programmed sets of reactions and emotionally driven triggers, which influence the way our body and mind perceive reality...

The boy pondered on this rather shocking data, thinking of his habitual patterns. Trying to understand them, he sat down on the sofa and picking up his notebook, scribbled a title on top of the page *of my habits.* After a moment of silence, he quickly added a smaller print next to the header *good and bad.* Letting his body sink deeper into the soft, a little too soft cushions of the couch, he stared at the page, his mind rushing through the patterns of behaviour in search of habits of any kind. *It's difficult* he pondered *because I'm pretty sure my mind doesn't want me to recognize some of them, especially the ones that cover my ego's aims.* The boy smiled imagining the ego within, similar to a scared mouse, squeezed between the corners of the room, its eyes widened with fear of anything that does not feel familiar and comfortable enough to just lay back and watch TV, *ego is a piece of work* he murmured. Realizing it will be much easier to put the habits onto the page chronologically, he wrote down each action his mornings bring, realizing that almost every step along the way, from the moment he would wake up to the time when his persona would enter his workplace, he acted out of habit. A multitude of them to be more specific. His mind glazed with sparkles of understanding, as he recognized the way he brushes his teeth, makes himself a coffee, or sits down to write is pretty much the same, each day, every week. *That's crazy* he sighed, looking at the page, which conveyed his morning, one could say, routine. Following the thought, he wrote out all the actions that are a part of his daily life. He decided to focus on weekdays as he considered them to be rather a substantial majority of the time spent here on Earth. He chuckled seeing his scribbles, so boringly usual, yet so essential to his existence. *Is my life really this boring...?*

*

Once the majority of the days, including the sporadic weekend activities, have been written down on the page, he leaned back on the sofa and relaxed his mind for a moment. *Now the hardest part* he thought, *I got to tell the good ones from the bad...* As he read in the same book, which advertised this statistic, it was also stated that each habit can be relinquished and created upon the consecutive, conscious choice of change.

The boy wondered how long it takes to create a habit, as well as how much does it take to take one away and release oneself from its influence. Taking his traits into consideration, he decided to read on the subject a little more and strive to create a positive change by freeing himself from the habit of oversleeping, at the same time creating that of a morning run and yoga. It felt great to make that decision and carried by the wave of initial inspiration, he researched the tricks to make a habit stick. Many sources mentioned writing the habit down, some invited the participant to create a timesheet of their day, others offered a hypnosis session on YouTube to get underneath one's skin, into the very space where our habitual reactivity was residing and making the changes there. The multitude of options and advice was overwhelming. It was so grand, that at some point the boy realized he has spent the past week researching rather than doing, reading on the subject, rather than taking the action to make any changes at all. This gave him the first practical advice for the future, which derived from pure self-expertise *if you want to change something, take action. Period.*

Taking on board a few different techniques, advertised both in self-help books and online, he decided to keep on researching the subject, all the while the action would be already in progress *better than just thinking about it any way* he summarised. With a month of experiments, he managed to stop hitting the snooze button on 4 out of 7 days in a week and achieved morning runs with a similar statistical amount. It was as if, when he would not hit the snooze button, he was already pretty much destined to run and stretch afterward. This has made him aware of the power that lays in making one successful step forward and inspired his mind to explore this phenomenon. After some more weeks of self-discipline training, the boy arrived at the conclusion that there was only one true and exponentially important factor, which was able to change the habitual activity of his and most likely that of others. It was persistence. Consecutive action, possibly in similar circumstances, performed again and again conditioning his body and mind to accept it as a normal, usual if you will, state of being. For example, the alarm was only necessary for the three weeks, as later, the boy would wake up at around the time of it or slightly before by himself. This, from his perspective, was a shift of a grand scale, as his sleepiness and overwhelming morning laziness was usually the case, the prevailing motif of his whole education career. Moreover, he realized that similarly to exercising, his morning writing became less and less difficult to conceive, as the conditioning was taking place on the daily basis. Like muscles, tensed and relaxed during a workout, which forces them to strain and build stronger for the next day, his mind seemed to give in more and more to the creative abilities, as his morning meetings with the page became a part of his daily routine.

*

The greater challenge in the boy's opinion rested in 'destroying a negative habit'. He recognized that there are more destructive hindrances to his activities than hitting the snooze button, therefore trying to understand how to undermine them, he kept on researching. Recognizing screen time as well as intoxication, like those which happened too often and tiptoed on the edge of overindulgence, he wanted to make a change in these areas, letting his mind focus more on the positive, progressive for his life activities. Starting with the phone, he decided to set up a time limit for each app, which was to help him realize when too much of his day went past staring at the small screen.

It helped to an extent, but as the timer would go off and announce *it's time to stop scrolling* the boy would often click the option *just a little more,* and ultimately not gain too much help with deleting his habit. Taking a step further, he created a set of rules for himself to follow.

*

Recognizing the morning routine being the most productive for himself and the evening being the time to rest his eyes a little, he created himself a schedule. Each day until the morning writing and run was done, he would not pick up the device. Each evening once the work was over and he was an hour away from going to bed, he would leave the phone on the side as well, letting his mind adjust to the lateness of the hour.

*

After many months of the pandemic, which enabled him to rearrange his days as he pleased, he managed to create a few very positive habits and override some of those, that didn't work for him. He was still a long way away from creating a perfectly ordained, productive, and empty of wasted time day, but his effort gave birth to better daily living and empowered his motivation to keep going and keep changing the way he was to live his life. *We become what we repeatedly do* the boy's mind reminded himself, each time he would try to hit that snooze button again

.

KNOW THYSELF

It's important to know yourself, to be aware of both the merits and hindrances one was blessed with, and to learn to live with them all…

The boy was pacing back and forth, his heart pounding away in the depths of his chest, his gaze jumping from one spot to another in a manner suggesting a rather irritated state. Pressing the phone to his ear, he waited for the connection to reach his friend's awareness. He had to have a chat. He felt like he needed to talk. With someone. Now. There were a few people on the street, as he tried to come to a stop, meandering between flowing pedestrians. His face a little reddened with the cold breeze howling across the town, as well as with the steaming blood bringing the temperate nature of his to boil. He felt annoyed on a deeper level and was aware he was to blame for it. Trying to lean on the windowsill and take a moment, he finally heard the sound of a connection made and his friend answered the phone, *what's up?* The boy allowed his legs to settle, twirling in their erratic movements, suggesting plentiful of emotional baggage still to be put down and let go off, as he attempted to settle the mind. *I am quite annoyed bro* he started; *think I need a chat…*

*

The two understood each other a lot, having been through many years of friendship and daily helping one another to digest the unexpected twists and turns of life's journey. The boy appreciated his mate, as he seemed to always let him speak his worries without a stop, providing a worthy insight into his thoughts a few moments later. He tried to act the same, recognizing that it was the most efficient and pleasant way of helping, and being helped, one could ask from a good acquaintance. The boy explained the intricate nature of his present state, recalling an earlier interaction he had gotten through with one of his friends. He shined a little light onto the irritation his body and mind suggested with all their might at the very time when the confrontation has taken place. His friend listened without interruption, allowing the boy to let the steam out until the story ended and the monologue stopped. A moment of hanging silence filled the space between them, as the listener digested the story with its details. Finally, he responded, *so what you're saying is you are annoyed cause they pointed out the truth…* The sentence, worded like a question, sounding like a statement, caught the boy off guard. Hearing the arising frustration, like a wave of an ocean gathering its power after the withdrawal into the sea, he reasoned with his friend's words.

There was a minute of annoyance, a second of hesitation, and a sudden flash of understanding, which made the boy blush even more, now from the feeling of shame rather than anger. The boy nodded his head a few times, dumbfounded by this sincere, to-the-point opinion his acquaintance offered him. *It's like the two sides of the same coin* his friend added, *we talked about this before; one represents your merit, the other your hindrance... The irony is, they are always together, balancing on the edge...* The boy pondered on the subject squeezing the phone in his palms, the steam of hot air danced in front of his mouth when he breathed. *It's like with anything* he spat out a few words into the abyss of the world, *without up there is no down...* The two fell quiet for some time, seeing the whole of the topic unfolding on the screens of their minds. His friend took the liberty of walking into the shop, and buying a few things, all the while the boy stood there, leaning on the windowsill, surprised with the absurd simplicity of the situation. *I got aggravated because it was within me already,* he pondered, *they just pointed out the obvious...* Thinking of the amazement his mind suddenly got struck with, he thanked his friend and disconnected. Walking back home, his heart much calmer than before, he thought of all the situations when blinded by our weaknesses, we consider the others being the reason for our suffering.

*

With knowing and recognizing our flaws, we are prone to save ourselves from pain, by mere acceptance and understanding of the process... The only things that can hurt our feelings are the ones we give attention and recognition to.

CHOOSE WISELY

I.   Make conscious choices and evolve the way your heart desires.

Every one of us, who lives on this tiny floating marble of a planet, has our own story, our idea for our future, and our challenges to bear. Effort, persistence, and passion are just a few out of many factors that play a major part in our little journeys. One wishes to set up a store, one wants to raise their kids well, one tries their best to become a better listener. All of our wants and needs emerge from the plane of self-fulfilment, which is inherent to any living being in this world. A tree will grow as tall as it can, a lion will achieve as much as it can to keep its pack safe and well, and so does any human unconsciously or consciously strive to reach its highest potential, as it is an essential part of life to evolve and become. A wise man once said, when one stops growing and learning, one starts to die.

*

The boy looked at the few lines of scribbles, which suddenly displayed themselves within his mind and appeared on the page in front of his gaze. He pondered on the meaning, trying to remember the quoted thinker, but without success. *I should probably start writing these things down* he criticized himself, feeling a little pinch of shame lingering behind his shoulder. He thought of the idea of potential, which interestingly for humans was very much different than for any other being. *A tree can be nothing else but a tree, a lion can do nothing else than a lion does* he counted, *but we can strive and achieve anything we imagine. We can become anything...* He scratched the palm of his hand and instantly heard reasoning devouring his point of view, *but you cannot be anything else than a human though can you* suggested the mind with ridicule. Shaking his head, the boy thought, *point taken, but we still can do so much more and be so much more than just eat, sleep, and reproduce...* He considered the potentiality of his life, taking into account different influences and experiences, which shaped his journey so far. *And there are so many possibilities* he added with a smile. His reasoning silenced for the moment, probably preparing another counter, he continued writing.

*

There is just one little trick about it all. With the choice comes responsibility the boy noted, *one that has the biggest influence on the outcome of one's life.* Nodding his head in the rhythm of the music, playing in the background, he pressed enter and started a new paragraph.

Each of us can choose what we commit our efforts to, meaning what we wish to achieve and strive for. This can be a huge obstacle, as most of the time, our decisions are far from ideal, therefore making the assumed task difficult. And if we count into the equation the number of influences and overwhelming noise of the world without, it becomes rather challenging to make any conscious and mindful choices at all.

Trying to calculate how many other beings played their part in his upbringing and evolution, the boy realized the probability of wrongdoings due to these connections and influences.

*

It is not that any people around us, especially in our childhood, are inherently malicious, trying to mislead or stop us from anything. It's just that as each perspective on the world and its works are unique to the individual, oftentimes the direction others see for us are not the ones that are ours to take.

Moreover, whenever one does start to strive towards a certain goal of their choosing, chances are there will be plenty of obstacles along the way, which might also side-track or discourage the efforts and the will to continue. There are two major steps in making this ability evolve the way we wish it to work. One, make the right decision, which sits right with your heart. Two, follow through no matter the circumstance and opposition.

*

The boy stopped his hand, letting the wrist rest gently on the desk, as his awareness raced through the waves of words that spilled onto the page again. His mind appeared to agree with most recognizing it being a little harsh, but ultimately truthful, to what his experience suggested. He focused his brain on coming up with a solution, a piece of subtle advice that could help others and himself adjust their aims and empower their evolution towards the wished result.

*

To know what the right decision is each step of the way is rarely easy, to be certain of the way one will achieve their goal can be misleading, and more often than not the true growth happens when there seems to be only failure around... He scratched his forehead, visibly boggled with the moral of today's writing. A flash of wisdom appeared at the back of his mind's cave, as he considered the possibility to scrap the page and give the creation of some story another try.

*

The only thing one needs to be certain of is where their destination lays. Such focus, persistent action, and a faithful, hopeful attitude will take care of the details.

*

Taking a deep inhale, the boy reflected upon the presented assumption, thinking if the words do not seem too glamorous for his humble work. His reasoning mind, the criticizing alter ego stepped in, feeling his weakness. *That's a bunch of crap* he heard its voice, *but it resonates with him so stay quiet and keep your negative attitude to yourself* answered his heart, its soothing rhythm of speech filling the wounded confidence.

As Wattles puts it in The Science of Getting Rich[2] - to think what you want to think is to think the truth, regardless of the appearances.

---

[2] W. Wattles. *The Science of Getting Rich*, Kindle Edition, Boston: Digireads Publishing, 2017

II. Isn't life similar to a game of chess...? On one hand, you're constantly standing your ground against the adversities of the day, on the other you got to catch the king...

The boy's eyebrows frowned intensely, the moment his brother placed the bishop in the middle of the board. *Check* he whispered satisfied. The boy observed his pieces, trying to come up with a good alternative for what was about to happen. He was going to lose the queen, that was certain, but he still had a choice for what price. Scanning the board, he calculated the potential of his move and tried to alternate the hypothetical future getting a few steps ahead of the game. He was in trouble. *Alright, then* he exhaled with a sour grin spread across the face and moved the queen to get rid of the bishop. His brother took out the queen instantly, *check*. Now there was the queen of the adversary threatening the king. *Alright,* the boy took a deep breath, letting his mind count the possibilities, *damn* whispered the ego within.

*

After the game, they played another one. Obviously. His younger brother won one of them, the boy won the second one. They shook hands on the draw and decided to take a break before going at it again. As his sibling left the kitchen, the boy picked up his notebook and wrote down an idea, which flashed across his mind's screen during the game. *Life is like a game of chess he noted, is it though...?* He tapped the end of the pencil against the tabletop, as his analytical mind, warmed up by the two games of chess, grinding the idea with its flaws and advantages. *Okay, let's see* his creativity exclaimed as he closed his eyes.

*

First, there is a king and queen. The king is the most important piece in the game, yet it is also the least able one, whereas the queen is not essential for victory, but without it, the army potential is heavily weakened. The boy's brain analysed the pieces as his hand-sketched phrases and sentences across the page in the endless movement of intuitive dance. *The aim of the game is to catch the king of the enemy, which could be transcribed to the idea of chasing ones' dream. In this sense, all of the adversary's pieces and moves are nothing else but obstacles on the way to obtaining ones' goal. The king can also be considered ones' integrity and commitment to such goal's attainment. Following this thinking, the queen could represent the skilful approach, as it is the ablest and most valued piece in the game. Without its range of motion and adaptability, victory is much more difficult to attain.* The boy nodded his head a few times noticing a certain method in the madness of his creativity's reasoning.

Then let's reflect on the bishop his mind whispered, *due to its ability to move across the board, setting up openings and inciting the opponent's reaction, the bishop could be seen as ones' determination and courage to create opportunities in the space where there was none in the first place. Sounds easier than it is* the boy murmured. *Then the knight* he continued, *a definite 'black horse' of the game... Due to its out-of-the-ordinary pattern of movement, the knight is a great example of ones' creativity and 'outside the box' thinking. With its help, we can set up a solid defence, as well as hidden attack patterns. Great asset to have up ones' sleeve.*

*

The boy straightened his back and grabbed the glass of water. Gulping down the rest of the refreshing liquid, he pondered on the validity of his mind's ideas. *There is no right or wrong when it comes to creative writing,* he reminded himself. Putting down the glass, he drew his gaze back at the page and decided to finish the discourse. *So, the next one to consider would be the rook* he started, *such an important figure both in the game and in life when seen from this thinking's perspective. It can represent the strength and focus on ones' goal, as it is a great piece to set the final strike with. The range of its movement is slightly restricted, but once unleashed in the appropriate situation, this asset is highly valuable. And finally, the last but not least the pawn* the boy noted, *as simple as this piece can be, it is of great use, especially when supported by one another. This figure is certainly a symbol of persistence and discipline,* his mind acclaimed, *one step at a time, one step at a time, this little, seemingly insignificant asset, can over time become the next queen, as well as provide the necessary set up when used with patience and confidence. The strength of the pawns lies in their ability to support one another,* the boy thought, *and although it is the first one to spare when necessity requires, it is also the only piece out of all which can turn the game around once it reaches the far side of the board.*

*

The boy observed the scribbles spread across the page for a moment, thinking of the reasons, which could undermine his words' essence. He pondered on the lesson learned today, one that could be drawn as a conclusion from his early afternoon discourse. *Care for your integrity, use your assets wisely, and don't ever underestimate the power of persistence...*

He thought of the sentence, which echoed through his mind a few times before; one that he read in the book, which treated on the life of Abraham Lincoln. *The good thing about the future is that it comes one day at a time* he remembered.

That is why we should always choose our moves wisely.

LEARN FROM FAILURES

I.   *Sometimes we just need to feel the pain and let it boil out of our heaving hearts...*

The boy was not okay. Sat in his room, staring at the wall with a blank expression rested on his face, he felt empty. There were no tears. At least no more tears, since he has cried them all out the night before, and after a few attempts to fall asleep, he realized it isn't possible and accepted the situation as it was. The sun came up, while he was still sitting there, motionless, helpless, feeling useless and far from acceptant to himself, for he knew what he has done is painful and hard to come to terms with. His skin seemed a little greyer, his eyebags a little darker and more vivid, his lips squashed together in a bitter expression of what one might look like, after eating the whole lemon including its skin. He felt lost as he has never felt before, or at least that's how it felt like. It happens sometimes. That is the moment of pain and suffering, we forget of all the previous, similar situations, which had also at the time seemed impossible to bear, and yet came to pass in the end. Bearing witness to this grief he felt, he wasn't happy to sit there like so, but he couldn't do anything else. He was just at a loss for it all, the motivation, the strength, and the drive to even move an eyelid. Sitting in the corner of his bed, his back slouched on the wall, his pillow resting on the floor beneath him without him taking notice, he waited for the moment to pass, letting this wave of uncertainty and suffering swallow his whole; like a whale whose overwhelmingly huge mouth was closing all around him, giving him not much space to escape through. The boy was grieving strongly.

*

The wound of his heart was fresh, but not as fresh as one could assume it to be. It's been a few weeks since the breakup and he considered it rather a closed subject already, yet since yesterday, he was hardly able to accept that it has happened overall. Something within him cracked and all the pain, which most likely laid hidden beneath the surface of his sea of consciousness, emerged, bringing an overwhelming feeling of sadness, remorse, and guilt, which filled the boy's heart with a great deal of suffering. *What have I done* he asked himself again and again, not accepting the notions that have emerged, *how stupid one has to be...* Feeling it all made him cry greatly, providing a platform for all kinds of accusations to come up and be expressed through his body and mind, leaving no stone unturned in the garden of his soul.

He felt hollow within, almost as if someone has intruded on his house and after stealing most of his belongings, left the door open with offensive writing sprayed over the outside wall. *Here lives a man who asked for this robbery* the writing claimed, *for he has refused the gifts of the universe...* The boy felt like self-harm isn't enough to pay for what his actions have brought to life. He struggled to stand his ground, as the darkness of self-doubt, despise and anxiety hovered above him. He wanted to die. *But would death be enough to pay for this all* he wondered, seeing his deeds listed on the accusation paper, spread across the floor of his bedroom, written in vividly red bloody letters, signed by the devil himself. And he saw that the devil's face was one of his own. And so, he grieved, wishing he could turn his head away and stop existing here and now, his pain relieved by the lack of any feeling. But this was not possible, as he was still alive and far from able to move, therefore even further from killing his existing form. Drowning in his sorrow, he stared into space, motionless.

*

The day has begun, his parents rushing up and down the stairs, packing away all the belongings, which they needed for the journey, their family was about to take. His mother entered the room, letting the boy know that it's time to start the day. He didn't flinch, his body curled in the corner, his mind spaced out far from this dimension. *Is everything okay* she asked approaching his diminished demeanour, noticing the dried-out tears and expressionless stare. His body tensed, as she laid her hand on his forehead *are you ok?* The question echoed through the corridors of his empty mind, like a scream, which flies through the abandoned rooms of the lifeless hotel. He didn't answer, his face's expression still lacking in colour and meaning. She checked his head, looking for the signs of fever or state of illness, which would explain such behaviour. He didn't feel it. Trying to reach his awareness, she looked him straight in the eye and smiled expressing her worries. Her voice flew above his pit of sorrow, offering a moment of clarity to appear between the depths of his shadows. Like an echo in the well, he heard her worries and wishes to see him better and more here, living in the present. *Whatever it is my son, remember it will come to pass* she assured him, trying to notice any reaction to her words. The boy's eyelids trembled, giving her hope, which she quickly acted upon, grabbing his hand, and drawing it towards her. *Sometimes life feels far from perfect* she said, *but no situation wouldn't pass... Come back to us my love* her last words resonated within the corridors of his mind, his face twitching for their sound.

He looked at her suddenly, his eyes gleaming with tears, his mouth trembling, *I have made a great mistake mom and I hate myself.* Her face flushed a little, her smile widened motivated by the wish to alleviate his suffering, she squeezed his hand stronger. *Offer yourself a little forgiveness, as you would to someone else that has done you wrong,* she asked in a soft, calming voice, *life is too short to hate yourself and we are too imperfect to make no mistakes at all. You are just a human* she drawn him towards herself and hugged his stiff body, *give yourself a little time to accept what is and draw conclusions of what was. Forgiveness my dear,* she whispered in his ear, *that is what everyone deserves…*

II.   *Is there a way of redeeming your past, when all that you have done has led you here, where the sunlight does not reach and the sounds of the surface fade away…?*

The boy fell so hard, his bones cracked with a loud echo spiralling up the deep ditch, he fell into. His pain was nothing in comparison to the emotions he was experiencing. No physical pain is as strong, as overwhelming, as immobilizing as the one caused by the suffering of the mind. He felt like crucifixion would be a walk in the park; like nails to the palms would tingle a little in comparison to what his overwhelm has dealt him this moment. Unable to move, he struggled to breathe. *It might be better to just die now* he thought, comparing the physical death to the unbearable spiritual suffering he was experiencing. Nothing seemed to make any sense, nothing seemed to mean anything worth making the effort to live. Silent as it was, in the deepest of the human-made ditches; the ditch of one's soul, he was lying curled into a foetal position, ready to dissolve into nothingness. But that would be too great for him; too good for his wretched soul and dirty body, which has caused so much suffering to the person he loved most. And why? What for? What was it that made him act upon those simple urges in the perspective of having what he had, with whom he had it? How does one scrape so strongly to crawl down the worst type of the sewers known to man – the sewer of lies and bad deeds. The sewer, to which no one would want to arrive, yet some try so hard to discover…

*

His mind spat at him again and again, leaving stains of bloody red liquid spurted all over his dirty clothing. He didn't feel like fighting it off. Any will to act or fight for anything has evaporated, leaving a dry, empty space, one that is the hollowest anyone could imagine, like an emptied bullet casing, which still smells of the gruesome effect of its actions. He was lost to all and especially lost to himself.

Unable to take back what he had done, unable to scrape away the dirt of his rotten hands, he suffocated with the thoughts of what he has lost and how he has made all the effort to arrive in this place, which so inevitably and fairly exiled his unworthy being. Trying to turn on the side, he felt his whole-body creaking and shifting in its insides, twisted of all the bad he has done. *It's only fair* he mumbled with his mouth completely immobilized by all the lies that have been stuffed in his throat for so long. Now with everything out on the table, he was forced to experience life with all that he has done, present in his body, mind, and soul for all the eternity screaming at him the worst expressions of the suffering he has created. There was no judgment in those voices, for judgment is not granted to those who fail to recognize the humanity of others. There was only despise and honest expression of what he has done, which led his being to this place of depth and suffering for what felt like an eternity. Scared of his own voice and the looks he would give himself when faced with his reflection, he closed his eyes and tried to squeeze the ears tight enough to stop the cannonade of sentences, which constantly arose within. But that wouldn't be possible, even with the ears cut off and his eyeballs gouged out, for the true judgment and pain came from the voice which could never be silenced, the same one voice which has advised him so many times to do that which he had done, neglecting the facts. That voice knew no remorse, couldn't tell bad from the good and was dependant on one particular aspect of the boy's existence, that of wish and desire, and through that, it was prone to fail and advertise anything, no matter the clarity and purity of the motif.

*

The boy scrambled to sit up and tried to take a breath, his heart pounding without stop, his mind screaming all of the worst remarks on his behalf, his throat straining to find any space for a little air. He wasn't able to do anything. He felt defeated by his worst enemy, himself. The one that knows all the dirty deeds, all the true and false perceptions of himself, the one that acts of the pure knowledge of what he truly is. And now, he truly was no one. Worse than the biggest scum of the planet, smaller than the speck of dust, an atom in the field of atoms, most useless and undesired of them all. He was not a human anymore.

With time and actions taken, which he has despicably used to his advantage, now he faced the most difficult and harsh trial of them all, the one of his conscience, which shaken so brutally, with all the might he was able to gather at those times of weakness, was nothing more than an angry, vicious and resentful dog, which came out of the shadow when he fell down the well, unable to move or call for any help. There was no help to find, as people know how to treat those, who do not treat others fairly. He was all by himself. Stuck at the bottom of a long way down, without the strength to fend off the ferocious beast, that has finally been given a chance to get back at his awful master, he looked his conscience in the eye, recognizing that this is merely the beginning of what he had to endure to become whole again, with all that he has done, there was no way out of the hole but that of a long, harsh climb, many weeks of suffering and the challenge of overcoming the biggest hurdle known to man, that of his past, which suffocating as it was, drawn the last breath from him, as he closed his eyes without a sound. The dog growled deeply and jumped towards the remnants of once a great man, now merely a stack of meat and flesh lacking in form…

III.   *How does one free themselves from the constant thought of remembrance and grief over the days that have passed…? How does one let go of the people they so dearly held in high regard…?*

The boy was able to sit up, pushing his bruised, broken back against the cold, stone wall of the well. He was no longer pushed to the ground as much as before, but the vitality was still far away from his organism. He was alive, that he knew. Looking up, towards the bright rounded spot, which hovered, what seemed like a lifetime away, above him, he tried to gather the strength to shout. A mumbled growl came out of his sore, dry, and filled with what felt like sandbags, throat. Scared of the sound he made, he flinched, pushing his back stronger against the only constant in his present situation – the wall behind him. He felt despise for his person, even though that didn't help his situation in any way. He felt deep sorrow, knowing what he has lost, he has lost forever. He tried to shout again, hoping the few tears of his eyes would water the dried-out surface of the mouth, providing the necessary sounds. He coughed instead. Spasms of the dry clank of a cough filled the quiet, echoing space in which his body resided. He felt defeated. Thinking of his wrong deeds, he touched the surface around himself. Uneven flooring, stony siding, and the humid texture of it all made him feel sick. *Look how far you've fallen* he thought to himself, letting the hands rest on his lap as faintly as the arms of a tree broken after the storm.

I do miss her he heard from within and shuffling in his seat he sniffled. He felt broken in a way, he has never experienced before. He felt broken from the inside out. Holding onto what was no longer with him, he felt the overwhelm of the hopeless monologue of his mind. Nothing positive, neither encouraging has been said, leaving a hollow hole in the middle of his chest widening, with each word of discouragement. *It is time to understand the mistakes and learn from them* he thought, *no one said learning doesn't hurt sometimes…*

*

Wiping his nose with the sleeve of the jumper, he didn't know the colour of, he looked around, straining his eyes to see through the thick darkness of the well. *Maybe something to help me up and out would appear* he pondered in a little strike of hope, which lasted no more than a gunshot's echo. Without success, he roamed his mangled fingers across space, in which his suffering endured. *No help* he thought, *why would there be any help for me anyway…?* The question seemed valid enough for the search to stop, giving way to yet another wave of sorrowful tears, which due to the dehydration of the boy, seemed more of a dried-out tap excavation, leaving a little memory of what once could have been a tear in the corner of his eye. He was no more able to cry, which somehow filled him with a greater sadness than before. His wish to cry is strengthened by the will to do that, which cannot be done. *Isn't it funny how the things we miss the most are the ones we cannot have or do…? Almost as if the ego didn't want anything easily available, or more so, what wasn't yet to be attained…?* The boy strained his throat to make a little sound, but nothing happened. He looked up at the hole in the space above, imagining the breeze and the sounds that were present on the surface, away from his place of sorrow and suffering. *How could I have been so stupid not to love you as you loved me,* he asked the silence around him, his words barely manifested in his sunken eyes. *Why did I let you go* he added, raising his palms to face each other, and folded them together. In the sign of prayer, he bowed his head slightly, *please forgive me, for what I've done.*

*

His head swivelled side to side, as he tried to keep it up, his neck muscles giving way to the tiredness of the body. He took a deep breath, floating his chest a little higher for a brief moment, his brain energized with a momentary inflow of oxygen, which so scarce in the space, disappeared promptly. *I must get out of here or I am a dead one* he thought, squinting his eyes, and moving his dried out, stiff lips, trying to accept the inevitable. He thought of his significant other and of the time they had together.

43

He thought of the moments of laughter, acceptance, and unconditional joy of being with that other person. He thought of the times when after a tough day at work, a struggle with studies, or a stressful adventure, they would hide their bodies colliding with one another, squeezed so tight they became one in the embrace of peace and happiness. He thought of the moments when it was hard and difficult to deal with something, sometimes offering each other more anger than joy, only to come back to the pleasurable time together moments later. *Forgiveness was so easy then* he thought looking back with melancholy to what was never to come again, *I wish we would be back where we were my dear...* He slouched a little more, feeling the agonizing pain overflowing his body, his demeanour diminishing slowly. *How should I forget about you now* he pondered looking inwards and exercising the will to see not only the good times but those less favourable as well. *For the sake of myself, I have to remember those times as well my dear* he coughed out his thoughts, offering more concise messaging than the spasms of his body. *I am sorry it ended this way he added,* mumble echoing towards the surface like a bubble of air accelerating towards the sunshine, from the depths of the ocean floor. *I did not deserve you* he cried, hiding his face in the arms of no one but himself, *how could I have let you go back then...?*

The well looked empty from the outside, no one around to even consider peeking inside. The boy was left to himself, his only hope being the salvation of his own, through the work within. But this was yet to come, first, the suffering had to take its toll...

IV.   *Depression can feel like a decompressed, overwhelmingly big bag of bricks hanging off one's back, as they go about their day, trying to stay sane and not pay too much attention to the weight above them...*

The boy has done wrong so badly, his legend has been shattered against a wall, similar to the mirror, which shatters in thousand pieces once met by a hammer. He was not who he thought he was, struggling to accept the facts, which written out in his mind's screen, like credits after a movie, were going back and forth expressing the despise he felt for himself. He has failed beyond all expectations and feeling the overwhelm of the feelings that became his everyday partner, he sat in the corner of his room staring in the space. Dim light around him made the atmosphere eerie, but considering the colours, which danced within him, the room might as well be considered a celebration space. His thoughts paralyzed him. Every time he felt the need or will to do anything, they came back with a doubled force, pinning his body to the mattress and offering no alternative to sitting down without an aim. His suffering was so deep, because of the nature of it. He was suffering the realization of what he has done to the person he truly admired, cared for, and loved. Now all that has been left from their once worthy relation, was the sour taste of his lies and disrespectful behaviours. It was the time for grief, but in a special, more excruciating way, as he was the one who made the killing. Again, and again, he has scratched the surface of their once-perfect glass, until his scratches managed to break the layer in half. The bridge has burnt, the ship has sailed away, the boy was alone. *Finally,* he thought he would have said, but it was far from what he truly felt. He was more than alone. He was without himself. The realization of what his actions have done to the person, he didn't want anything bad to happen, he stopped accepting himself and the feel of overwhelming, impending doom has greatly grown. He was no longer loved, neither by her nor by himself. He felt as if the hope of anyone ever loving him, has gone with the wind, leaving a hollow shell behind. In that shell, his body existed, vegetated, decomposed. He didn't feel human anymore, he felt stale like old bread and mouldy like leftover food. He felt unworthy of anyone's look.

Starting for the door, he felt the needle pinch in the back of his heart. Ignoring it at first, he took another step and felt it yet again, a little stronger than before. His mind still agonizing with thoughts of his love, didn't seem to bother. He took the third step, ready to start the day, overcoming the feeling of nothingness and uselessness but something cracked. A part of his heart broke and he fell to his knees instead of reaching the doorknob. His heartbeat disappeared as quickly as he managed to lose all he cared for. He felt the pain shooting down his spine and landed on the floor in a momentary spasm of agony. He tried to breathe, but with no success. He tried to move, but without effect. He gazed into space, his mind still wandering about, his eyes stiffened, fixed in one spot. He knew something bad is happening but didn't know what. His hands faintly lied, lowered to the ground, his arms twisted in shapes like a grapevine wine, he felt a slight pinch, within or without, he made the last breath and fell into night.

*

It didn't take long to realize what happened. The police were taking care of him, deciding what to do. His mother and his siblings stood at the door crying. *Is he going to be okay officer she asked, or is he dying?!* The policeman turned around, looked at the sad bunch, approached them without rushing, and offered his hunch:

I believe madam that the kid lost his heart he claimed, he seems to have been granted the heaviest of the doubt, the doubt in the existence of himself at all, he is no longer with us, neither is he with the deadly foe. He is barely between the earth and the sky, he will not get back up quickly, until he pondered, until he knows why. Until he knows what he's done, until he accepts the failure of his actions, he won't see much of the worlds' daily attractions. He is barely alive, for his physical body knows a little less than the mind, and agrees to embody, what he once was, neither a cheater, nor a lover, no fool, he was just but a boy, and for that he will soon regain all his ability to move and to act, but the healing on the deeper level, that is a fact, will take longer to heal and to accept what was done, because no one gets away with unpleasant fun.

*V.   Can a beggar become a king the same way a king could become
         a beggar?*

The boy pondered, while sat in his place of isolation. His hair messy from many days of not paying any attention to his looks, he scratched his forehead leaving a spot of ink from his pencil. His hands, dirty of all work he has been doing for the past weeks, have become a miserable sight. He looked around his surroundings, scanning the room for any hope or salvation as if either could just appear on the wall or manifest itself in an item of God's choice. The room looked as miserable as the boy, the state of it far from favourable, its corners dusted and filled with randomly abandoned possessions. *How does one get back to what was without letting go of what is…?* The question filled the line, leaving his heart as quiet and shy as it has been lately. He didn't feel much these days. Every moment of his day balanced on the edge of grief and complete misery. The misery of a sort one can only experience when their life flipped upside down has nothing more to offer. His cheeks browned by the long-lasting dirt offered a few cracks of clarity, where his tears have managed to flush the layers of abandonment down to his collar. He didn't bother to look into the mirror. To be specific, there was no mirror to look at. With a conscious choice, he has covered the only mirror in his flat, with what was left of his decorations. *Nothing to see in there but misery* he reminded himself, whenever the worry of his outlook came into mind. His eyes sunk with shaded bottoms, his cheekbones sticking out as they never have before, due to over excessive dehydration and lack of proper eating, he looked more like a ghost than a human. *This is how yours truly looks like nowadays* he mumbled, seeing the one he so longed for at the back of his mind, *will I ever get your appreciation again…?* Scribbling the words on the paper, he flipped the page, letting the new part of his story begin. Hesitant of what the next part should be, he sighed out loud and looked out the window, where life continued as it always does. *No time is spared in this constant flow* he reminded himself, *not for a beggar, neither a king…* Thinking of this paradox, he looked beyond the walls of his mind and imagined himself nowadays in comparison to how he perceived his person back a few months ago. One image drew the signs of vain and hopelessness, one of those of high hopes and chased dreams. Neither was fully convincing to him, as he barely considered himself a person now. *Anyone could be better than this he thought, what am I if not a shadow of who I once was…*

*

The pen touched the surface of the sheet and the boy started writing. *There was once a beggar, who strolled the streets of his town minding his own business. His coat resembling his state of mind was far from clean.*

He might have not been happy with where in life he was, but years of taking care of essentials have taught him to appreciate the little things and discharge any of the desires that were outside of his reach. He was content to be how he was, numbed by years of pain to the point when the pain was no more an issue. His feet once covered in blisters, now only tough and rough gave the expression to his essence. He was ready for anything and hoped for nothing. Going about his day in a manner that ignored anything out of ordinary, he spent most of his days in self-pity and letting go of that same feeling straight away, sometimes with a help of a bottle or two. Years passed, his beard grew, and he subconsciously became the shadow of a person, leaving all he once was behind. He didn't pay much attention to anything, taught by experience that there was not much he could have hoped for anyhow. One day, while going through town, as he usually did at this time of the day, he noticed a girl standing by the coffee shop, reading a book, and waiting for her coffee-to-go to be made. Struck by her presence, he stood still and stared at her, his mind blank as never before. He observed her lips, as she read the words of the page silently, making a few flinches now and then. He studied her hair, which floated on the wind and fell onto her arms in cascades of the dark brown waterfall. He savoured her pose, so relaxed and self-confident in its calmness. His heart struck a chord his mind did not recognize at once, but the longer he observed her, the more understanding of it all he became. The girl flipped the page and most likely felt the gaze, as her glance at him echoed through the halls of his heart and filled his mind with fear and shame. He felt bare as if standing naked on the street where everyone could see his mind on the plate, his weakness embalmed in the tough skin exposed to their mercy. He blushed within and without, his hands trembled in the empty pockets of his coat. She studied him for a moment and looked away, as her coffee was finally made. She didn't bother to look at him again, walking away towards the seaside. The man stood there stricken with all the might emotions can strike with, knowing nothing but the overwhelming weight of the need to follow her and do all he could to make her see him. Whatever the cost he said to himself, whatever the cost... He followed her to the seafront and observed which bench will she choose for herself. Once seated, she continued the read, sipping her hot drink with noticeable satisfaction. He stood there for a moment and instantly making all the decisions in the mind needed for this wish to happen, he rushed away towards his friend's barbershop.

*

He asked for a shave, which surprised the owner considering he has never come for a shave before. He didn't explain his motifs, just mentioned that there is a change he wants to see, and now is the time to make it happen.

After getting his face and hair to a state, he continued through the streets and entering the local charity shop begged the owner for a pair of shoes and a shirt, which could be exchanged for the coat he wore. The wish didn't appeal to the man, who asked for payment but once he saw into the eyes of his, he quickly accepted the payment in the later time and gave him what he required. Determination written on his face; the man continued the makeover with time hanging over him like a shadow. Remembering the place, where he would sometimes go to take a shower and refresh himself, he wandered through town energized with the feeling stronger than any other known to man. Showering he whistled, which surprised him as much as frightened, as he realized he is caring for something in his life, and knowing how painful it can be to care, he wished for his heart to give him a break. The heart isn't a servant he reminded himself and prayed for the first time in many years. He prayed for her to be there; he prayed for her to give him a chance; he prayed for himself not to die of this feeling he was experiencing. He walked fast, even though he felt like running. His body felt strong, despite the dire state it was in. His spirit was there for the first time in so long he felt like his life is not what it was anymore. He didn't want to be a beggar, apathetic to all that happens. He cared now.

*

Approaching the seafront, he prayed for her to be there for a little longer. Turning around the corner he believed its possible, he wanted to believe it. How great was his disappointment when he discovered she was gone? He ran towards the bench, looking around in a panic, his gaze scanned the area with agitation engraved in the irises of his eyes. Feeling the wave of hopelessness and disappointment filling his guts he sat down on the bench, resigned of his fate. I hate hope he sighed, it plays with your mind...
Walking back to his place of isolation, the bridge underneath which he so frequently drowned his existence in bottles of cheap cider and drugs conceived with the help of the locals, he held his head lower than ever before. More transparent than ever, he felt lack of existence was his state. He walked towards the bridge, seeing the people on the street enjoying what he seemed to understand as life, so far beyond his reach. He saw couples gazing at the sea, the kids with their parents running around the park, the working men driving home to their happiness. He felt alone as never before, the flicker of hope and love becoming the pain of his heart, which seemed to drown in tearful blood of the mistaken understanding. He was about to cross the road when the dark hair flashed in the corner of his eye, somewhere between the pedestrians walking down the avenue. He instinctively looked towards it and without much consideration sprinted across the street, seeing the jumper that he so vividly remembered.

He ran across the first lane, his face flushing with the smile of hope that once crushed was present again. He screamed 'wait' and seeing her head-turning he cried with happiness. He didn't know what he was going to do, he didn't know even how he would do it. He only knew he wants to make the step, which would take her to consider him and see him in the light he has seen her in. He ran across the road, as she looked at him surprised; her face expressing fear and sadness. He didn't understand for a moment what she means with this gaze, quickly realizing what was happening as the horn of the upcoming truck echoed throughout the street. His mind wandered off shortly after the impact touched and transformed his life once and for all. The vision of her face was the last thing he has seen, and lying there, mangled with the accident, his body faded away, the smile and flicker of hope still present on his blood-covered face.

*

The boy dropped the pen on the floor and folded the hands on the desk. His crying was silent as it always is when the pain is too heavy to bear. His heart cracked and crashed. He felt as if his story finished similarly, only to see the ending of it sometime or never…

VI.   *It is no easy task to discuss and reason with yourself, especially when the 'gut' feeling suggests you're in the wrong…*

The boy was a little sad lately, enjoying his everyday adventures just a tad less than one would assume when observing the smile on his face. *Isn't it so easy* he pondered sometimes, *to just make a smile'*… Times were different and as a major change happened in his life, he found himself struggling to keep the positive attitude, which he was so often highly regarded for. His walk seemed a little slower, his springy steps a little stiffer. His gaze seemed to wander more than before and his attention span noticeably worsened. He felt like he has faded away ever so slightly. *Like a plant taken out of the pot,* he sometimes observed, *or a ghost whose house to haunt in has been demolished without notice.* These feelings were tightly connected to the change, which shook his 'normal' and as anyone could anticipate, has put him completely out of balance. He was lost. Spending the days, the same way he would, regardless of the status of this aspect of life, he has quickly discovered that things have shifted and are seemingly worse than they have been before. Even though the change appeared to be a good idea at the time, once done, it was causing him a great deal of suffering, with which the boy reasoned, trying to understand himself and the way he arrived in this situation.

There are so many reasons why I should have done what I did, yet none of them seems viable in the light of the emotions I am experiencing the boy pondered, hitting his head against the wall again and again in the search for the meaning of it all. *How does one free themselves from the shackles of the past without ripping out a little from the future* he asked once, sitting on some empty street after the night has come in and scared all the life away, *isn't what I am experiencing but a consequence of my ideas of the future and the present dying in my arms like a bunch of acorns, unable to grow as they have been flushed down the sewers...?*

*

Talking with one of his friends one day, the boy tried to express his worries and feelings about the situation in search of resolution. Holding this friend in high regard, especially in the connection to their knowledge of the human mind, he has confessed his actions and explained his motifs, hoping to gain a better understanding of himself and maybe, just maybe, to achieve a level of peace due to his friend's advice. Listening to his story, the friend sat quietly nodding her head occasionally and asking a further question at times. He shared his expression of what was, as well as his belief of what could have been, with her wise mind, and after a moment of settling in with what was said, she decided to answer some of his perspectives. *First of all,* she started, *neither of you are to blame, and both of you are, at the same time. Life sometimes just happens like that...* She opened her arms, her palms facing the sky, and took a moment to organize the latter part of the answer. *Think of it this way* she said, *you have done what you thought was right at the time and she has done the same. Even if it doesn't seem to be the right choice from the perspective of time, it must have been the best choice you both had at that particular moment* she continued, *neither of you has had ill-willed intentions when those situations took place... It was like dancing at the party, when you are too drunk to bother, you dance purely instinctively and sometimes that means you will break the vase by accident. Did you plan to break it...? No,* she concluded, *it was just an unlucky accident due to the circumstances. You cannot blame yourself or her for taking that sidestep without noticing the vase. It just so happened that it was there when you waved your arm...*

*

The boy thought long about his friend's words, putting the answers together and reflecting on his ideas and perceptions of the situation he found himself in.

Sitting in his room, looking around at the items, which inevitably, through association, were to cause him arising thoughts of the love he has failed to hold, he considered the idea that all that is happening has its cause and effect, and by taking refuge in this concept tried to relieve some part of his suffering. *How does one accept a situation, which his mind does not accept at all* he asked quietly, sitting in the space so dearly held in his heart, now so overwhelmingly empty, as if someone has taken all the furniture out. *It feels like there is a part of me that has been carved out with a blunt knife and left somewhere on the way, making it impossible to put it back inside* he thought, holding his hand next to where the heart is. *Hollow* he mumbled, *that's what it feels like to lose love…*

*

A few weeks went by as his struggle continued. In the mind of his nothing changed at all. His pace of walking still slower than before, his smile so forcingly worn that the corners of his lips seemed to have both upright and downward curves, his gaze still shaded by the memories of tears occupying the surface of his eyes. He met with the friend again. It was not planned to talk about the situation once more, but as life has a way of making things happen, this was one of those times when it all just folds into place for the greater good. The boy sat in the park with the girl, talking about their daily routines and fun times they had last year during vacation. His mind meandered between the good and the bad, making it apparent that at some point he should express his pain to his friend, in the hope of gaining some additional advice or relief of a sort. After a while, his friend as wise as she was, asked the question herself – *so how you are doing these days, you know* she paused, *with all that…* The boy pondered for a moment collecting his thoughts and coming up with a way to answer this rather wide and deep question. *Oh, you know* he started, *I am grateful for our talk last time, but I would be lying if I said I am much better these days…* She nodded; her attention fully focused on his expression. *I feel hollow* he continued, *as if a part of me has died or was cut out without a chance to be brought back in… It hurts…* His voice broke a little, as he looked away, gathering his strength to finish the sentence. *It hurts to think that a part of me, that was created through the time spent with her is not going to be back here anymore* he said, *feels like I am grieving.* The girl nodded tilting her head slightly and smiled with kindness. *Your description sounds perfect she started, you are pretty much in a grief mode and yes, a part of you has left without going back… It will take some time to convince your mind of this and to get over the pain, which this space has caused…*

She stopped for a moment, putting her hand on his arm as he looked up at her, his eyes a little brighter than before. *But think of it this way* she concluded, *you had a great time together, you gave each other so much and in a natural way it ended... So be it. Now you have a space within you that is empty, which means it can be the space to grow and be filled with something new. And who knows* she paused smiling, *maybe this is going to be the greatest adventure you have been waiting for...*

RESPECT YOUR TIME

Creating the space for ourselves, to do what our heart's desire, equals giving ourselves the space to be the way we were made to be…

The morning routine did not go to plan. Prolonged slumber and silenced alarm clock made the boy's day difficult to start. He stood in front of the desk half asleep, looking out on the brightness of the day. *I overslept didn't I,* his mind seemed to suggest, *did I though…?* Confused and still very much so unconscious, he pushed the power button of his laptop and decided there is only one way to pay back for his crime of lack of discipline – work. Writing out the first paragraph, he heard the waves of drowsiness splashing at the back of his brain, his body awakened abruptly only started becoming aware of what was happening. There was a certain magic in the act of creation, which he so longed for whenever work of the day, the same one which paid for his bills, was not creative enough. He didn't know much about the world, only that it was a vast, rather strange, and overly populated space, but even less did he know about himself. He was aware of the name, given at birth, the age and ancestry, which followed him manifested with his looks, accent, and passport book, but there was so much more to him, which went unseen wherever he went. He anticipated it must have been the case for each of the people stuck on this little marble of a planet everyone calls Earth. He didn't know what it was he ought to be doing most of the time. He struggled to recognize the reasons for doing anything at all, and most importantly he didn't know what his purpose was. *Why am I here* he pondered often, *and why am I here now…?* Explaining the purpose of the world around him seemed easier*, it's here so all of the species can live* he would deduct, *it's here so I could live…* But trying to recognize his own 'why' drew energy from his brains without giving much of the answerback, and he didn't like that. *Maybe we are all here to create our why* the thought suddenly struck the mind, causing his palms to stop their dance across the keyboard, making his heart instantly stronger in its pulse.

*

He pushed away his chair and walked across the room to grab a biscuit and a cup of water, *no coffee for you yet* he hissed in the mind, reminiscing the late wake-up call. Swallowing the cookie in one, he sipped water slowly looking at the workspace, which felt like a part of his world more than most of the things visible outside the window. It felt special. Sitting back down, he noted the thought for later and went back to writing, trying to unpack the claim, as if one's why was to be created by oneself.

Sounds quite philosophical he smirked undermining his thought, *watch out for mister mindful everyone...* He smiled softly, letting the Inner Critic silence, and got back to tapping away the ideas, without giving much attention to doubt, which always present, liked to creep up behind the screen whenever something original to the previous pattern of creation entered the story. *Nothing more reliable than one's doubt* the boy chuckled, learning to ridicule his thoughts, whenever the connotations suggested a negative motif. *It's as good of an idea as any other when it comes to one's purpose* he added, *who knows what's theirs anyway...?* Trying to reason with his way of thinking, he considered the factors which participated in his daily life, shaping the outlook on the world through his mind's lens. *Beliefs, expectations of mine and others, experience-based conclusions* he listed, *idealized futures, hopes and anticipated worries, emotion-driven reactions...* He looked at the words and confessed within, that truly there is much more of these, yet most come down to one of the phrases already mentioned. *That's a lot of sources* he nodded his head, digesting the information, which dripped from his person onto the page like blood drawn from the infected wound. *And all of them are partly there to suggest the 'why'* he realized and challenging the theory started ticking off each phrase, which could have influenced his own 'why'.

*

Having ticked off each word on the page, he shook his head in disbelief, realizing just how little of his outlook on the world depended purely on him. *It's as if someone would fill the whole room up to the ceiling with presents and once there is no more space asked what you want for Christmas* he thought, *and even more so the presents of all type should be constantly arriving at the door... More and more with each program, ad, discussion, interaction, and event in one's life...* The boy pondered on this little analogy, trying to find out the reasons for which the assumption of the situation was to be faulty. There wasn't much to argue with, *we live in a time of information overflow* he concluded, *no wonder it's so difficult to answer a simple question of 'who am I'.* Realizing that there is an equal value to taking in and taking out, especially regarding information, the boy decided to cut a few corners. *No more scrolling through social media he claimed, no more tabloid news... It's time to stop hearing all the 'why' around me and find my own... It's time to respect my time'...*

KEEP JUGGLING

Life is like juggling five balls while riding a unicycle, with a sloth stuck to our back and balancing a sword on our nose at the same time.

The boy was sat at the desk, considering this abstract picture, which reflected his perspective about life's experience. *For everyone it is different* he thought, *yet the same in its variety of form. Kids and those that do not have responsibilities, which are crucial to the survival of their life, are allowed greater freedom of choice between the actions possible. That does not free them though from the juggling essential to the process of life. The stakes are lower than those of the responsible "adult" life, but the decision-making and constant need for activity stay a part of the daily life for everyone. When one becomes of age or is put in a situation that calls for accountability the stakes shoot up and ask for a response, which chosen consciously or unconsciously, sometimes through habitual behaviour, impacts the present, as well as the future of the individuals' experience. Juggled balls represent in this scenario our primal needs, which are of the main significance to the existence of the juggler. Need for safety, nutrition, ability to rest, source of warmth, and feeling of being loved are the balls, which always require a part of the performers' attention. The bicycle itself represents staying on track, which provides self-validation, the pursuit of ones' dreams, and active living to the best of ones' ability. Our rider is the Self that keeps control through self-reflection, self-appreciation and healthy (both physically and mentally) living. This part can be seen both as the help and the obstacle on the way to self-fulfilment due to a passenger, whose presence we can feel on our backs at any given time. The exemplary sloth is the fearful small self, which is commonly considered to be the ego of an individual. This safe-loving entity likes quick pay-outs, long breaks, and comfortable space without any trouble or grind. Filled with anxiety towards action taking and risk of any kind this passenger can be the juggler's biggest opponent in the performance of life. Last, but far from least, the sword represents the idea of the Self, which differs for everyone holds the key to ones' happiness, success, and fulfilment of life. It is both a blessing and a burden to ones' existence. While holding a great value of joy and achievement, it is also the source of the greatest pains and troubles... Be it the love to a person, ambition for a successful career, or beating ones' record the sword encompasses all the possible wishes of the greatest value at any point in life. Possible to change with or without the initiative of the juggler, the sword is what existence is called for in the present; it is what makes life worth living.*

And as it can be different to everyone, it is true to all that such personalized sword exists and is present in the performance of 'the trick of Life'. And so, the act continues unstoppably through the force of change, chased by the time, and cheered for by the Unknown.
Remember to keep juggling whatever the costs… the show must go on after all…

REFLECTING

'Learn from yesterday, live for today.'

~ Albert Einstein

LAW OF ATTRACTION

I.   *Ask and it shall be given to you; seek, and you shall find; knock, and it shall be opened upon you... Three simple pieces of advice on how to navigate one's life...*

The boy stared at the little paper he carried in his back pocket for many days, which became crumpled and torn in a few places. It was still the same piece of paper he has prepared to carry around a few months back. A scribbled set of phrases from the Bible preached their wisdom, as the boy read it out to himself now and then. There was something about these words he didn't quite understand at the very beginning, taking them on board of his routine with a pinch of salt, sceptical about the whole fuss around the supposed substance presented within. It took him some time to comprehend the meaning of them, making the whole set stick together like nothing else, his mind treating it more and more as a given set of rules rather than an advice list. He tried to recall the cool anagram, that he once heard about the Bible, *basic instructions before leaving earth* he remembered, and smiling a little, he got up to take on another day of work and effort. His life became very mundane in its core, as he had to tackle the isolation time on his own, stuck in his tiny flat. The thing that kept him happy and motivated hanged on the wall above his desk, *goals to pursue* the title of the big sheet of paper announced. The boy who was spending most of his days at the desk looked up at the list often, keeping the flame of hope fiery and energetic, which was to help him get through this season of the world's little break, without the risk of wasting time doing nothing. He didn't like doing nothing. It made him feel useless and unhappy from the 'get-go'. He recognized that the three rules set by the Bible's wisdom applied to the 'non-doing' as much as to 'the doing'. One provided asking and receiving, one lack of asking and lack of receiving. *Simple as that* the boy would often remark.

*

He noticed that his life gained momentum with each decision made in the direction, that was somehow aiming at one of the goals written out on the list. It seemed important to pay attention to the choices and decide upon them promptly to keep the dynamic of the progress steady and on the growth side. He wanted to see more of the results he noticed now and then. Most of them were barely visible to anyone but him, but that did not matter. What mattered was that his perspective and belief level-shifted, each day providing a stronger flame underneath the burning desire. He knew what he wanted, roughly, and he was getting more and more convinced he will get it.

Day by day, decision by decision he would remind himself; *we create our reality.* Appreciative of the amazing words that were shared thousands of years ago with someone, who was inspired enough to write them down, the boy thought of how crazy the journey of these words was. This recognition made him contemplate the nature of things, the cycle of life and death, and the constant advancement in the creation of the world around him. *For millions of years,* he would sigh, *for millions of years, it's been going on, non-stop… How crazy is that…?*

*

Taking these words to heart, he thought of all the stories of his life, when through the effort of looking, asking, and pursuing certain things, he managed to gain them regardless of the initial appearances. He thought of the championship in kickboxing, which came after mere three years of training, while most of the time he was just focused on practicing more and more. He thought of the jobs he worked, starting in the worst corner shop there was and finishing the last two years in one of the best jobs available for a student in the whole town. He recalled the time, during his first year of university when before the first competition his coach at the time invited everyone to choose a song they were going to play while walking into the final fight of the championship… *The walk-in tune* the boy thought back then, how *cool is that…* He remembered he made a choice back then, he knew what song it was going to be, and he knew he was going to hear it there someday. It felt absurd at the time, but that never meant impossible…

*

Thinking of these situations; breaking them down into small steps and achievements along the way, the boy realized the true meaning of these few phrases, that every person on earth should understand for their own sake. *You can have, be and do whatever you desire* he acclaimed, *all you must do is ask for it, pursue it and be open for its arrival… Period.*

II.   *You cannot get anything for nothing, that is just how this universe works…*

The boy was reading a book, written by a doctor from India, who surprisingly became a spiritual teacher after recognizing an alternative way to treat his patients. Learning about his story, he thought of the idea presented with the statement drawn from physics: *no energy can be destroyed, it can only be transformed…* Trying to understand the nature of this concept, he sat back on his sofa and closed his eyes to let his thoughts see more clearly, undisturbed by the outside world around him.

*

The main claim presented in the book concerned the possibility of creating and attracting anything one desires into their life based on exchange. *Nothing can be acquired without giving something in exchange* the boy recalled and thinking of this potentially true statement, reflected upon his present situation. For his earnings he had to give his time and effort, for the good physical health he exchanged hours of exercising and proper eating, for his friendships he offered time and kindness to those who became his acquaintances. Looking at those aspects of his existence he struggled to find a reason to doubt the statement. In the book, the author invites to give gratitude for what one already possesses to receive more goodness into one's life. The boy pondered on the idea, and acceptant of lacking arguments against its correctness he decided to approach it with an open mind and try it for himself by experimenting. He was going to write a list of ten sentences of gratitude each morning and night for at least two weeks.

*

In the beginning, the whole action felt rather unnatural and a little annoying, as the boy yet again added himself a task to execute morning and night, which, in his already over-filled day plan, was inconvenient. Nevertheless, he kept with his attempt and over the first week managed to make the evening and early day listing into a little habit. He didn't see much of a change at the time, as the true discovery was still to be found. Somewhere around the second week, the boy noticed that his overall mood shifted slightly. He felt more contempt with his days and smiled a little more than he used to, which as surprising as it can be, wasn't proof of anything just yet. Continuing his experiment, he wrote the thoughts down and kept on with the decision to finish the test before jumping to conclusions. Time passed, and the last week was about to end.

Having noted down different observations of his behaviour over the three weeks, the boy went back to the book again and realizing there is not enough explained in the book, to provide him with an elaborate explanation of this *giving to receive* phenomenon, he took his time finding sources of the author's speeches online. He committed some of his spare time to give them a listen and dotting down few scribbles of notes here and there came to the conclusion, which opened a new door of perception for himself.

*

Firstly, he recognized, that by mere noting of ten good things that took place in his day or life overall, his focus on noticing those little gifts became stronger, therefore making himself more aware of these happenings taking place. Simply put, he was consciously and subconsciously looking for these things, to have them written down twice a day, which made him notice them more often. As small a shift as it was, it provided him with a great deal of additional joy and proved to be quite a pleasant addition to his daily routines. *My overall mood has improved* he noted, drawing the line underneath the last date of the experiment. Reflecting upon the thesis stated in the book and revisiting the talks given by the author, which he found online, he concurred with the correctness of the statement. *By giving my time to see more of good happening to me over the day* he claimed, *I felt better and more well-treated by those days... It's almost like I've given my attention to the goodness in exchange for receiving it, therefore receiving it more, or at least more consciously...* The discovery wasn't ground-breaking but gave the boy a solid base to build upon when trying to attract different aspects of goodness into his life. He thought of the issue of abundance, focusing mostly on wealth, and remembering the statement *the rich get richer and the poor get poorer* and putting it in the perspective of the rule of giving to receive, he wondered: *maybe what this phrase draws the attention to is the fact that those who are rich-conscious will notice more riches, therefore, attracting more of it into their life, whereas those who are poor-conscious will notice more of the lack, therefore, attracting it towards theirs...*

*

Knowing he has found some logic behind the statements and recognizing that Einstein himself drew upon the idea that energy can only be transmuted, it cannot be destroyed he decided to continue his gratefulness pages daily and looking for more sources of knowledge about perception, he researched the books worth giving a read. *If there is anything that one can control in this world* he thought, *it is the process of one's thinking...*

Keeping this in mind, he wanted to learn more about how to create the life he wished for. Right here. Right now…

III.   *The universe is so vast, filled with so many stars, which seemingly insignificant brighten up this dark ocean of space…*

The boy pondered on the sentence, sipping a hot tea from a little cup, which he held in his folded hands in the manner like that of a praying man. His hands were cold, warmed softly with the heat of the brew, making him shiver slightly as he kept his gaze up at the clear, starry sky above. The clouds were nowhere to be found, and as the sun went down the greatness of the cosmos emerged, flooding the ocean of the night's sky with bright dots of all sizes. The boy was sat on his own, listening to what seemed to be the silent soundscape of the night in the suburbs, far from the turmoil of the city, the lights of the streets absent, letting him experience a great feeling of oneness with the universe, as the sky emerged in all its glory, without the light pollution from the surface. *It is so difficult to enjoy the night sky these days* he thought, remembering all the times he looked towards space without the ability to see more than the moon or a few stars, *our civilization may not have conquered space yet, but we managed to pollute it…* He sipped the warm liquid slowly, holding it in his mouth before letting it fall down his throat. This simple pleasure of tea-drinking never bored him, letting his mind settle for a moment. The boy thought of all the times he stared at the sky with his father by his side, during the long nights of the winter, whenever they could go on a 'skiing getaway'. Those times long gone, he reminisced of all the beauty and gratitude he should have enjoyed and felt in those sporadic times of peace and quiet, not understanding its value at the time. *I was so young than* he thought. Time passed. He grew up and moved away. Few years passed, times changed, and his father struggled with money more and more. His company failed. The boy looked at it from afar, feeling the need to help, helplessness filling his throat, as he heard his youth idol expressing his worries over the phone. *Don't think we'll be able to afford it* he would often say with a loud gulp within his throat as he did. The boy felt annoyance at those times of weakness, struggling to accept the changes his family had to make.

He wanted to help but was far from able to do so. He struggled to make the ends meet himself after all. *I have a few thousand to spare* he said to his father once after his savings account grew substantially during the quiet time of the year, *let me help you.* But his parents didn't want his help – *it's not much for our worries and it's all you have my son* his father answered, leaving the feeling of hopelessness to overwhelm the boy. He sipped the tea slowly, letting a single teardrop down his cheek. *Acceptance* his teacher's words echoed in his mind, *acceptance, and hope.* The boy was determined to change how the world was but as he grew up, he understood it isn't as easy as one might anticipate. *There are things prone to change* his teacher would mark, *and there are things that change won't touch until they change themselves.* The boy savoured the wisdom of the teachers who taught him throughout his life, and as he grew older more and more of those words of wisdom resonated with him on a deeper level. He agreed with some of them and refused to accept the others; some causing him a lot of grief as he went through the years of experience in this wide, wild world. *The world owes us as much as we owe falling stars,* he repeated the words of a song he often listened to, during his studies. *You don't get what you deserve, you get what you negotiate* he noted another lyric, fighting the hopeless feeling the first sentence has caused.

Trying to piece the whole 'truth' together, he often found himself wondering what the universe represents in the sense of this variety of approaches to what life is and does. *What if we make our definition of what the world's dynamic* he pondered, *and the universe just assist in its creation...?* The idea empowered him slightly, letting the steam out, filling his gut with the powerful joy of hope, which suggested that there might be a little if any chance to change the circumstances he found himself in. He thought of all the times his actions have influenced the outcome, remembering how people of the past have conquered their situation and created the present he lived in. *Much like the stars in the sky* he thought looking upwards, *each of us shines our light in the darkness of the universe... Maybe this brightness, unlike any other, determines the light we bring to the world around us...?* Reinvigorated with this idea he sat back in the foldable chair, letting the slightly warm tea rest on his lap. His hopes and dreams flowed slowly within his mind, as he leaned back in the chair, staring at the starry night. *It might take some time* he thought, *but if we are like the stars, our light will shine forth one way or another... After all,* he concluded, *we can't be hopeless being as alive as we are...*

IV.   *Aren't we all the heroes of our tale, just sometimes forgetting to play the main role...?*

The boy heard an expression in one of the podcasts he listened to – *don't be an extra in your movie.* The speaker, a very charismatic older man, asked the listeners to take charge of their lives and become the hero of their own story. The boy pondered on this idea, considering his situation. *Am I a hero or an extra in my life* he asked himself. Marching through the rain towards the shop, he was lost in thought, counting all arguments for and against both options. The weather was far from satisfying, and it did feel like a proverbial Monday morning. He crossed the street, skipping across the small puddles of rainwater, and navigating between the bigger ones he approached the shop; his thoughts still entangled in the web of the presented concept. He pulled out a bandana from his pocket, tied it over his nose, and entered the local once more reminding himself of the absurdity of the times he was living in *a pandemic they call it* he muttered. People of all ages rushed through the shop lanes, taking their essential shopping with extreme care, moving away from others around them, and throwing scared glances at those, who 'didn't keep their distance'... The boy felt for them, thinking of how hard life must be if you live in such fear. With his usual shopping list, he took care of the essentials and crossed the alleys arriving at the till. The whole task didn't take him more than ten minutes.

Once out of the shop, the bag weighing on his shoulder, he continued his contemplation, letting the mind whisper its ideas and perspectives into his inner ear. He thought of the situation that recently dawned upon the whole world, as he knew it. The 'pandemic', which was advertised as the biggest threat to societies and lives in ages, brought upon the daily life restrictions and rules, that disabled more than half of the activities needed for people to stay healthy and in a good mental state. He hated the way mass media contributed to this situation, considering the amount of misinformation and negativity they constantly poured into the minds of everyone who decided to pick up a newspaper, tune in with the radio or just turn the TV on. He saw it everywhere. The constant noise of troubling, scaring, and misleading news that overwhelmed the population, led to this feeling of fear all around, wherever one could go. *People stopped engaging with each other, they stopped caring for others, they stopped living...* the boy thought. There was plenty of statistics and graphs spread all over the internet, without much attention being given to understanding their true value and the information they carried.

*

Most of the citizens don't even double-check the news he thought, *they just listen to one program and think they know 'the truth' he smirked sadly, how crazy is that...?* It wasn't like he didn't understand there was a virus out, he could believe that. What he was concerned about was the likelihood and severity of its spread as well as the ultimate influence this whole situation had on every other aspect of human life. He ground his teeth, when his father shared the sad news with him, announcing that due to the poor state of the company, he had to sell the family car. He felt pain listening to his friends, who lost their jobs due to restaurants and cafés being closed and going bankrupt because of the lockdown. He felt it all too heavily and recognized it was building on the issue of the disease in the first place. *Yes, we should protect the vulnerable ones* he thought, *but surely there is a better way than putting the whole country on hold and letting people lose all they have in the meantime, as we wait for the 'silver bullet' of some sort...*

*

Putting it into perspective, he reached the flat and climbed the stairs to enter his living space. He left the shopping on the kitchen counter and approached the notebook, willing to write down a few ideas that came his way during this little shopping adventure. He thought of the initial impulse, connected with the statement made in the podcast *who is a hero and who would be the extra he pondered.*

Looking back at the thoughts that sprawled in his mind as he did his shopping, he concluded that people, who decided to let their lives be led by these mediums of mass-media and reactivity are 'the extras in their movie', whereas whoever takes care of their life separating his emotions and thoughts from the overall fear and feel of doom could be considered 'the hero'. He sat down by the desk and picked up the pen to note this thought down. *I think it's more complex than that though,* a doubtful consideration echoed through his mind. *It's not like we are either the hero or the extra* he claimed, *I'm pretty sure we constantly balance between the two.* Noting down the idea, he reminded himself of another thought that has recently manifested itself at the back of his mind *there are two parts to our Selves, one high and one low.* He stretched his hand over the page, remembering the exact words he used expressing this concept to a friend, *with every decision we make in life, these two Selves, high and low, need to take up a fight inside, and whichever part wins, it gets to choose its favourable outcome. Isn't this how we go through the whole life* he pondered, *constantly deciding and taking up the battle of the two inside of us, over and over again...* He liked the representation of this process, as he described it. *There was a saying* he remembered, *there are two wolves inside of us and the one which wins is the one we feed more...* As he noted down a few thoughts and let his imagination visualize this pair of wolves inside him, he leaned back on his chair and folded the notebook on the side of the desk *time to get to work.* He has recently drawn a lot of knowledge from various books about success and considering the topic, which he heard in the podcast, he decided to act upon these straight away. *I am the hero of my story* he affirmed his position, writing down a list of goals for the year, the month, and the week ahead of him, *otherwise what would this all be for anyway...?*

TAUGHT BY NATURE

I.   Isn't nature amazing in its glorious perseverance, no matter the influence of the human hand...?

The boy sat down in front of his desk, opened the laptop, and written down a sentence, which came to his mind as he watched the outside world in its glory. The sky was blue, pure, clean of clouds, which only spontaneously drifted past his view. He noticed the moon, half of it to be more specific, still hanging in the distance as if the day coming to its existence didn't bother it. *How come you still here where I can see you* the boy pondered, *aren't you supposed to be engulfed with reflected light in the night's sky on the other side of our globe...?*

*

The sun came up, shining its beams of life energy across the landscape. The boy looked at the roofs of the houses across the street and realized one of the chimneys is alive. A small bush, not bigger than a little tree, has pushed its way through the holes between the bricks and became a part of the construction. He could see its little flowers, opening their petals towards the sun, as if the building, the concrete, the bricks weren't there. *Where did you put your roots* the boy asked, knowing that the answer isn't anywhere to be found, *amazing...*

*

He pondered for a moment, thinking of all the influence humans have on Earth; their shovels, machinery, and production of synthetic materials becoming a part of the world they came from. *Nature always prevails* he concluded. There was a little moss on the side of the chimney, a tiny stalk of what might have been a tree trunk seen under a microscope laying its texture alongside the wall. The boy's imagination took him to consider how the world would look like if suddenly all the people would vanish. *Wouldn't that be something eh* he chuckled, *wouldn't you like that Earth...?* Certain that as much as all of us (humans) are a part of Earth the way another creature, alive or essentially dead is, he considered the idea again. *No,* he claimed, *you like us here... Maybe not what we choose to do sometimes* he thought remembering all the pollution, destruction, and changes that hands of those in charge made, *but you like us anyway... Who doesn't like their children after all...?*

We are nothing but slightly bigger ants that got a thumb to work with and a little improvement to our brains, so we could create and not only run around on repeat, as if programmed... But the longer he thought of the concept the less colour he saw in it. *We do act like programmed sometimes* he considered, *almost as if the white screen was our king...* The boy recollected all the time when acting upon a feeling, which triggered by one thing or another made him act a certain way, which not necessarily was the best one to choose, and felt disappointment. *How come we let ourselves go so much* he pondered, *we should look at nature and learn from it...* Wherever the human hand stopped its actions, nature came back to life. Sometimes it pushed through despite the influence our beings had on the spot, such as this little bush growing on the roof across the street. So out of place, yet so majestically right in its choice of action. *As if it knew better,* he thought.

*

He wished for more reason and resourcefulness in the minds of those, who decide where to start the digging and where to leave plants alone. *If only we knew better.* The sun beamed inside his little room, smudging its beams across his face, making his eyes squint. He felt its warmth; vitamin D rushing through his veins, filling his body with more motivation and inspiration to create, love, and act the way Universe would appreciate. With more empathy towards creatures of the Earth, there would be fewer wars, less abuse, and more freedom of space and choice. *We started chasing the coin and forgot we are chasing the very creation of ours* he concluded, *it's like chasing the precious cup across the room while trampling the whole porcelain set in the process...* He knew that money in itself was not bad. Nothing in itself is inherently bad, only the way it is used or considered might make it seem unfavourable in the perspective of survival, sustainability, and abundance, which encompassed the whole universe.
How can we feel there is a lack of anything if it only takes a stroll in the park or a run down the seafront to realize the variety and richness of the world around us, he thought, we truly are losing the grip on reality...

II. The term 'second nature' never really felt right for the boy. *Surely, he concluded, nature should be considered in the first place, when discussing anything that humans have ever experienced, discovered, or created...*

The boy pondered on the two words, that clamped together were to represent one's ability to easily fulfil tasks that one is used to. He looked up the term's meaning and writing down the statement, which seemed a little farfetched, he sat down in front of his notebook and looked at the written poems, which scribbled with energetic movements of the hand reminded him of his father's handwriting.

*

Is that a part of my second nature then he wondered, *or is this just another representation of how much influence a parent has on a child...?* His fingers tapped the desk rhythmically as his mind processed the idea, *what is my second nature then...?*

*

His considerations took him to recall the aspects of his life he lacked skills in, as well as the ones he was easily successful at. He thought of the abilities that seemed to simmer through his childhood upbringing, such as the constant extraverted chatter, tendency to stay lean rather than gain weight, and short-tempered attitude towards the teachers, annoying colleagues, and his sister, *I was not an easy child for sure* he recalled making out a little smile of empathy towards the lost soul he once was. He pondered on his early age successes of leadership, easiness in acquiring new languages, and the ability to squeeze out a good amount of knowledge from his brain whenever the risk of getting a low grade appeared on the horizon; he didn't like to lose, of that he was certain. Taking all these thoughts and organizing them within his still fairly young mind, he concluded that there must be at least a dozen 'second natures' of his, both with the positive as well as negative connotations. *Isn't it like that with anyone though* he murmured, scratching his unshaven chin. *Which one is the 'second' one then* he pondered, *and is there any first one...?* Writing down the two words, which started the whole debate, he leaned over his notebook and noted a little scribble next to the phrase *nature was here first.* He smirked, considering adding a word of a vulgar connotation next to it, but decided not to, as he knew it is rather inappropriate to offend others, regardless of the opinions they share, *it wouldn't add anything to it any way* he reminded himself.

He looked outside the window, where a little bush kept growing on top of the roof opposite his house, *keep fighting my friend* the boy whispered, addressing the nature's child, who opposed the human intrusion on his land, *you were here before us anyway...* That was the main reason why he didn't appreciate the statement and the connotations that came with it. *It sounds like we (humans) are first, and everything comes second,* he thought, *yet haven't we just recently showed up...?* He wasn't a genetical expert, neither was he experienced in studying world's history on a deeper than a public education kind of level, but he recognized that what has been happening with the term nature, and how its value has been diminished over the past decades, made him annoyed at and ashamed of his species. *We are destroying our own home at the same time calling ourselves the kings of the fuc...* he stopped the word and took a deep breath, *call ourselves the kings of it all...*

*

His neighbour from the roof seemed to appreciate his concern, as its leaves shook in the wind sending a little wave towards the frustrated earthling, whose mother appeared to need love, which was so hard to find these days. *Nothing that a little awareness campaign and people's movement couldn't help with* the boy pondered, *the only problem being no one gives a damn these days. We all seem to just worry about ourselves, forgetting of the Earth, which when dead would bring us all to the end as well...*

*

The boy shook his head, letting the emotions of irritation arise and leave his body. With each energetic movement, he released the tension within. Looking back at the written words, he thought of the possible 'second nature, which would put nature first and with it the wellbeing of all creatures in this world, humans included. *We should develop the habit of caring for Earth around us to such extent that it becomes our second nature* he noted below, saying it out loud as the words appeared on the wooden-extracted paper. *We are of nature* he exclaimed; *how then can we forget about the importance of it...?*

III. Nature is the greatest teacher on the planet, but only to those who are willing to be taught and listen…

The boy exhaled deeply, finally having the big assignment of the week finished, only two weeks after the initially planned deadline. He sat on the floor and took the phone out of the pocket, choosing one of his favourite public speakers to listen to. Devices connected; the sound of an audience filled the room, as he set the portable speaker next to himself and decided to lie down on the floor with his gaze softly hanging on the ceiling. He needed to rest taking the mind of the troubles, that he came across in the past month. He needed to reset. The speaker came upon the stage, as the initial applause silenced. The boy allowed his eyes to close and taking tranquil breaths surrendered to the spoken word.

*

A few ideas were conveyed in these thirty minutes' worth of material. The speaker left the stage and the recording ended, as the boy opened his eyes and pushed himself to seated. There might have been more concepts portrayed by the speech, but he heard four quite distinctively and decided to write them down before his memory would fade. Sitting at the desk, he ripped a piece of paper out of the notebook and scribbled the title of his note, which although not said by the speaker, seemed suitable and the boy wanted it commemorated. *Nature as the greatest teacher* stated the line. He underlined the sentence and chose a different pencil to signify the difference in the notes. Putting down four dots in a vertical row, he wrote down the parts of the speech that so significantly stood out for him, during the listen. *Learn how to handle the winters* claimed the first one. *Learn how to take advantage of the spring* stated the second one. *Learn how to protect your crops all summer* followed the third. *Learn how to reap in the fall without complaint* announced the last line. Scribbled words connected into sentences became a part of the boy's note and satisfied with the remembered quotes, he decided to ponder upon them, making little notes on separate sheets of paper for each aspect of *the four lessons of life from Nature.*[3] Taking out a few crayons, unused for so long, now so necessary, he signed each scrap of paper with a relevant lesson number and started writing down the thoughts.

*

Learn how to handle the winters the boy murmured, *that was something about difficulties.* Checking with the speech recording, he drew a few conclusions and wrote down three bullet-points underneath number one.

---

[3] J. Rohn. *Life and Lessons is Like the Seasons* (on YouTube)

Get stronger, get wiser his pencil announced on the white paper, *and do not wish it was easier, rather wish you were better…* Notes filled the lines, as he summarised the thoughts. *Fair points* he mumbled, as the piece of paper, joined the pile of inspiring ideas.

*

Skipping to the second point, he listened to the recording again, letting his mind fish out the necessary information. Inspired by the points made by the oldish man in the suit, who presented his views, he wrote down the second set of advisory bullet points. *Learn how to take advantage of the spring* the title claimed, hanging above the three dots splatted by the boy's crayon. *Take advantage of the opportunity, do something with it* he scribbled beneath, *do it now rather than later.* Nodding to himself, he acknowledged the wisdom surrounding the statements. Fiddling with the third piece of paper, he looked through the recording again, trying to recognize the needed points made. *Learn how to protect your crops all summer* he murmured, as the words offered their presence on the page, *meaning learn how to protect your plans and what you care for…* There was little if any hesitation within the boy, as he made the note, and slamming the paper on top of the others he got to the last one. *Learn how to reap in the fall without complaint* echoed through his mind, as the red crayon, reminding with its colour of the autumn leaves, stated the rule on top of the page. *Learn how to take full responsibility for both successes and failures* he noted below, *do not blame, diminish, and make excuses.*

*

Few points were made, he turned off the video and sat in front of the pile, which conveyed the way his brain worked in these times of high input high output. He used small pieces of paper to gather information and let his mind off the hook sometimes; letting the wooden surface keep the thoughts he heard and wished to remember for future use. Usually, it took him a few hours to go through his notes, once the pile was too big and overgrown space it was assigned in the corner of the desk. The technique was far from perfect. But it worked.

*

Coming back to the initial thought, the boy lied down on the sofa and looked up at the colourful tapestry of the tree, which hanged on the wall. *Grounded like the root, flexible like the branch, and strong like the trunk* the boy thought, *that is what a tree would say during this kind of a lesson.* He chuckled.

75

To be a good student one needs to learn to be taught but even more so, one needs to learn to apply the knowledge gained the boy claimed, reciting overheard phrases. *One step at a time* he sighed, *one step at a time…*

III.   *At the beginning of any creation, there was an idea…*

The boy was deeply moved by the new documentary, which a known British adventurer has created as his final testimony and a call to action. The motion picture is treated on the subject of climate change and the destruction, which we (humans) have committed against the very planet we came to life on. Sitting, with his arms clasped around his legs, in a position similar to that of a foetus, the boy let go of trying to stop the tears, wetting his collar with salty expressions of sorrow and disappointment. *How could we have let this happen…?* The scale of destruction and probable future presented in the movie touched him deeply, causing the heart to object, and raising anger within his chest. He wanted to do something about it, he wanted this to change.

*

Once the crying stopped, as the well of his painful tears has dried out, he got up from his bed and picked up his notebook writing down a few thoughts that stood out to him. Dotting down some ideas he suddenly got stricken by one, which ironically wasn't either negative or upsetting, but rather uplifting and full of hope. His eyes flashed with excitement, as he saw at the back of his mind the creation, which this idea could bring to existence. The note was brief and vague, just the way first-time concepts are. *A board game 'Saving Earth'.* He looked at the words, scribbled in a hurry on the piece of paper, which often participated in his thought process, sometimes helping with shopping lists, sometimes with work-related notes. There was a flash of light, which seemed to resonate throughout his soul, as he realized this kind of thought can truly materialize and become successful, considering the subject it was to touch upon. Invigorated, he ripped the corner of the page with the sentence written on it and slammed it against the wall of projects he was currently working on. He remembered from the books read while planning his own business, that it is important to give the idea the time to grow; for its seeds to sprout within the mind before acting, which is why after pinning it among other random words and concepts, he left the house to go for a walk.

*

A few days passed since the idea became a note on the corner of the notebook's page.

The boy got on with his daily routines; working in the office, taking care of his writing, and creating his online platforms with the hope that one day they would bring him funding to pay the bills. It's not like he didn't appreciate his day job, he even liked it, but deep down within he knew that his life will not be as fulfilling as he would wish it to be until the bills for the house or food needed to be paid from a nine-to-five hassle; it just wasn't for him. His parents would ask him from time to time what it was, that he planned after finishing his year of work at the University he recently graduated from. He didn't know for sure but, more and more, he was convinced that there was an alternative way to make money, far from the daily jobs, which sucked the energy out of the workers, making it impossible to enjoy the 'after work' time, as there was not much life energy within him after the full day of screen time. He loved to write and with the inspiration from his favourite authors and a few self-help books, he realized that the potential for his day job to be changed into a writing-based one was always there, and it was a matter of time until it comes to fruition...

*

One day once finished with work, the boy headed back home, his mind occupied with the plans of what to eat, as his stomach screamed and squeezed within, begging for a little something. Suddenly, a continuation to the idea of the game struck him. He stopped in the middle of the pavement, his mind disassociated from the body, as it made the extreme effort of catching the whole idea, which floated above his consciousness for that split second. He quickly took out his phone and noted a few random thoughts in the note's app, trying his best to describe them in the most approachable and understanding, for the 'future him', manner.

*

He rushed home, trying to hold onto the vision that has manifested in his mind, and running into the flat, he grabbed a pen and a big sheet of paper. He sketched a few lines with descriptions noted between them. He had the outlook for the game already. Looking at the paper, which reminded him more of a maniac-kind-of-drawing, he smirked remembering that his sketching skills are far from artistic. Excited with this new piece of the puzzle, which just like that echoed through his mind, he wrote down a few notes at the bottom and decided to take a little time today to think of it and come up with some outline of rules, which would be incorporated in this board game of his. Standing over the piece of paper drops of sweat visible on his temples after running up the stairs and wrestling not to lose the thought, he felt satisfied and victorious; triumphant.

77

He knew this creation of his was coming into existence and believing that the idea and execution are already there, somewhere beyond his sight at the moment, but closer with every day he spends thinking of it, he felt at peace. *It's just a matter of time* he sighed, sitting down on his couch excited for what was yet to come...

WITH LOVING KINDNESS

There is a certain magic in the act of helping another, which when manifested can take the individual higher than the physical realm enables us to experience...

The boy skated home with the wish to change his clothes, grab some drinks, and return for another night filled with the smoke of the bonfires and chatter of friendships forming around him. He has been on it for five nights straight, and at this point, he loved it too much to give it a miss. *There is a certain beauty in gatherings around the fire* he pondered *like we are becoming this fire that connects us...*

*

Grabbing his warm jumper, which already smelled of a marinated smoke, he ran out the door and followed the street on his board. He felt a little wobbly due to the earlier drinking but was able to hold his balance reminding himself of the idea, which his friend once presented that "only when fairly drunk, one knows how to skate properly". *Probably not* the boy reflected. With his foot rhythmically stomping against the asphalt of the street, he made it through the main road and arrived at the gas station, reminding himself to get some wood before reaching the coast. *There is never enough wood in these times* he pondered, *one more pack won't hurt...* How happy was he to discover that the prices on the station are lower than those at the shop he used previously. Feeling a little tipsy, he tied a red bandana over his face, covering the nose and mouth, and entered the shop pointing out the jokes behind the idea of wearing a bandana inside any shop or a bank. The clerk was an older man and once the boy recognized the price bargain, they laughed for a moment about the possibility of seeing each other often, as the boy announced to be back for more. He left the station with a bagful of wooden pieces and a beer for one of his mates. Skating down the road with ten kilograms of weight he recognized how the speed of his gains due to the additional baggage. He was at the beach in no time. There were bonfires all around. Students of the first, second, and higher years were all present in this pursuit of a little socializing time in this year of constant isolation and public life restrictions. *You can feel how happy they are to be here* he thought looking at the groups nearby, whose laughs echoed against the vastness of the ocean.

*

Approaching the bonfire, which his friends invited him to join, he left the bag next to the kindling and introduced himself taking a seat.

One of the organizers was amazed by the fact he has brought the wood, but the boy didn't say much to it *it's only fair* – he thought. There were a few people he met before and so the conversation with them was a pleasant one. Opening his heart more and more while the levels of intoxication grew, he met a few new souls and enjoyed the discussions of all kinds. *AMC has their bonfire at the end* his friend pointed his finger, *you might want to go and say hi...* The boy considered the idea and decided to take it. Leaving his present 'tribe' he walked across the plague finding another group of friends. What a surprise it was to find a group of people he knew on the way as well, *the world is a small place...* He greeted his friends from the year before and joined them for a little chat about the whole situation that seemed to prevail in their lives nowadays. A few moments passed, as the boy was considering the magic quality of fire, which gathers them closer and closer as the night becomes colder when a girl from another group approached asking for some kindling. He looked at her confused, not knowing by then what the word meant. *Sorry, I don't know* he answered, but willing to help he asked for an explanation. She must have felt a little awkward, as she left saying *it's fine. I can help* he thought, his body acting on a yet unrecognized quest, as he approached the group from which the girl arrived. *What's the problem* he asked looking at the fire, *which was about to die.*

*

Our fire is almost out announced someone without much hope in his words. *They seem a bit down* the boy thought and looking back at the fire, which he and his friends surrounded, he made the call instantly. Without saying anything, he walked back to the fire where his friends sat and asked one of them: *can I take a bit of fire for those guys,* he waved his hand intentionally. He knew the answer already. He knew his friends. Accepted by the nods of theirs, he picked up a log surrounded by flames and carried it halfway towards the other group. *Whoa* someone exclaimed in fear of being burnt, *it's fine* the boy answered. Leaving the log in the sand for a moment the boy realized he has grabbed the burning part and his hand sizzled with pain for a moment. *It happens* he thought with a smile, realizing that he 'is playing with fire' once again. The group welcomed his effort with smiles and quiet appraisals. *Enjoy your night* he answered and walked away back to his group. *What a powerful experience* he thought reflecting on the emotions he felt as his action was done, *beautiful to help another... Almost like bringing a flame of love* he pondered, sitting down at the bonfire with his friends. *Good man,* his friend patted his back, *bit crazy but...* They laughed heartily leaving the act in the past.

Time passed, and the boy went back to the other group, promising to be back soon enough. Sitting back down by the fire he decided to make the extra effort of speaking with new people, considering the magical quality of meetings around the flame. He spoke with a few fellow students, exchanged his point of view with one history enthusiast, and discussed the languages of different parts of Western Europe. Leaving the bottle empty, he felt ready to make the few additional 'good deeds' as he called them, hoping that it will inspire those around him to take that extra effort as well. He picked up the trash around their fire and walked off to check the bonfires nearby. How surprised he was to find two full cans of beer and a bottle of lemonade, which must have been abandoned by those who have been here before. Such a waste he shook his head disappointed and picking up what's left of the trash around he made his way back to his friends. *We'll enjoy them beers for sure....*

*

Their wood was almost done, and they started shivering against the midnight breeze. *It's time to join the others* he announced and taking a few people along they made their way to the bonfire at and of the coast. His friends welcomed them with an open heart. *It's good to have friends sometimes* he pondered, looking around and realizing how comfortable he felt in the moment. *Beautiful feeling,* he announced silently. Remembering what the story was with the bonfire earlier, he decided to go for another 'clean-up stroll' to spare the ocean a little bit of trash, *there is enough inside already* he reminded himself. Using the bag from his previous purchase of wood, he walked over to the bonfire he so happily supported a few hours earlier and discovered a few pieces of trash, which looked much better inside a bin bag. Picking up the leftovers, he approached another bonfire letting the graceful act of cleaning sink into the minds of those who saw it. *Be the change you want to see he recalled, and hopeful of the inspiration his act might encourage he kept on cleaning up. Bro* someone's voice drew his attention, *is that you, brother...?* He looked towards the speaker and noticed the man he met a few nights earlier. He smiled and nodded, *nice to see you, man...* The wave of the hand welcomed him to yet another group of strangers whose bonfire was already long gone. They huddled around the leftover ashes, which seemed slightly warm. *How are you* the boy asked aiming the question at the guy he met before. *I'm good man, how are you* a classic answer followed. The boy started the chat. They talked about the other night and the fact of cleaning up the beach being a bigger problem these days due to all the bonfires.

He quickly noticed that there are more people around him that he knows and considers acquaintances at the least, which made him feel happier and comfortable in the space *the world is a small place* he recalled once more. Coming back home after the time spent with so many different people, he skated down the main road, his head wobbly of all the alcohol intake, his legs a little cold of the stone seating for many hours. He felt happy. Realizing the magical quality of the fires that seemed to be 'the new black'; at least until the clubs and pubs won't open to the public again, he felt at peace with the idea of spending his year in this little town surrounded by like-minded people, who would choose to socialize around the bonfire. *It's like going back in time to when people lived in caves and had a tribe to defend,* he thought, *we are still tribes these days… We just have too much stuff to surround ourselves with and forget sometimes that the tribal instinct prevails no matter what… We are a part of higher consciousness in those moments of helping one another* he decided, pushing against the street with the wind in his hair.
We're all one tribe after all…

THOUGHTFUL CONSIDERATIONS

I.   *How does one change their view on the world, when the view is so strongly embedded in one's upbringing, social conditioning, and experience...?*

The boy was sat in front of a map, thinking of the idea that the paper conveyed. He thought how similar the world's true layout is to this one, presented to him and others again and again throughout our lives. He felt uneasy, like an animal who feeds on leaves and grass, while the predator makes its way closer to the unaware prey, with the feel of alertness being triggered within the simple brain. Recent events have drawn the boy's doubt to the surface of his mind. He no longer believed everything he heard, without seconding the opinion with questions, assumptions, and as people call it – 'a pinch of salt'. He didn't want to 'just believe'. The crucial moment for his doubts to start came not long ago, as he encountered a troubling opinion that the map of the world - the way it is made and promoted, does not reflect the actual state of the Earth's layout. He watched the video, and once it finished, he pondered on the subject, recollecting all the time his education depended on this depiction of the map. He wondered how true anything can be if ultimately it is something taught by another human being. *Isn't everything until proven with one's own eyes a mere depiction of such thing through someone's point of view* he thought in consternation. He felt that doubt suddenly covered most of his views and ideas with its cloak of uncertainty. The boy no longer knew what to believe and trying to reason with the idea that someone would purposely embed a false factuality into the worlds' understanding found himself wondering about the possibility of such concepts. He thought of the history, which taught in school was such a big part of his understanding of the present situation. He thought of the sentence, quoted from the past, which stated that 'history is written by the victors', and tried to remember the creator of such phrase.

*

Turning inwards, he pondered which parts of what was taught to him does he believe most strongly and reasoned why does he believe in them at all. *What makes something worth believing* he asked himself and opening a tab in the browser looked up the world's map. The search engine tumbled the information and presented him with a few different but quite similar images. He analysed them while making mental notes of other 'truths' of his life, he does doubt sometimes.

There is no chance I could make a conscious choice here and now, whether this is 'the right way' of depicting the world, he thought *I don't have enough knowledge in the first place…*

*

Everything is relative he quoted another and moved onto a different page looking for information about the map's credentials. Internet was full of information from random sources, which led him to think, that there either must be an organization that takes on board the idea that 'until proven true, any information cannot be considered right and therefore all of the worlds' knowledge would have to be reconsidered objectively and without any agendas', or most of what people are being taught is relative and subjective. The boy reached for his forehead shaking the head slowly. *No organization in the world is objective about anything* he sighed, *every person possesses subjectivity of their lives…* He concluded that there was no solution, which would enable any information to be verified against the facts without being influenced by anyone's wishes. The boy thought of a simple story that would depict this issue. He remembered the parable, which he heard from one of the spiritual teachers of his decade. The story presented an elephant, which stood in the middle of the room, as the six blind men were brought to participate. Each man was asked to approach the elephant and based on the sense of touch describe how the elephant is. Every man, one by one, described the elephant through the part, which they touched. One mentioned wide ears, one the elephant's strong legs, and another focused on the trunk. Each man was right in their way, but the true shape, size, and essence of the elephant itself were much greater than their opinions separated or even brought together, as there was more to the elephant than all of the men mentioned could realize. The boy thought of this story and recognized the truth in its symbol.

*

The elephant he pondered, *can be anything in the world that one tries to comprehend… And though all might be looking at the same thing, or experiencing the same sensation, each will tell their version, true to their perspective…*

*

This thinking did not satisfy his worries. If anything, it brought them closer to his heart making the uncertainty cloak more of a carpet, under which the boy felt overwhelmed.

He pondered on the thoughts that manifested in his mind and came back to the question, which triggered the whole situation. *Only through one's experiences,* the boy reasoned, *only with our experiences, we can tap into the 'true' nature of things. All other is but a direction, a perspective proposed to us by others...* He felt better coming to think in the certain way about the subject.

*

Doubt felt heavy; his worries of the lies he reaffirmed throughout his life, of the 'false truths' he repeated, all came down upon him making the body shiver with overwhelm. Thanks to the conclusions he encountered, his heartfelt brighter; more vibrantly fighting off the heaviness of it all. He looked at the map again and pondered on the idea that this, like any other map, should be considered only as a 'certain perspective' and therefore the doubts surrounding it would be much more in place. *Doubts for the soul are like pain for the body* he concluded, *they inspire to action through suffering, but in themselves should not be considered a problem, rather a way to progress in life.* He thought of the moments when he would burn his finger, get cold while underdressed, or 'tap out' before his arm's pain would become unbearable. All of these moments were triggered by the system of nerves that warns the body, whenever the issue arises, letting us change the circumstances on the spot to alleviate the pain. Similarly, to this, thoughts that provoke our minds to wander and ask questions are merely stimuli for change and action; in themselves being useless and leading to nothing, if one does not regard them as an inspiration rather than an issue. *So, we act upon our situations, stimuli, and truths* he thought, *only to arrive at the next stage of them, with new doubts, solutions, and ideas in-between the two. Like a never-ending dance of right and wrong,* he concluded writing down the sentence in the library of his mind. *Maybe Shakespeare was right to say 'all the world's a stage'* the boy wondered letting himself relax a little more with the presence of all doubts, seen now more as 'partners in crime' rather than the crime itself. *It is good to doubt I suppose* he thought, *because there is no problem in asking a few questions on the matter, even just as a conversation topic.* He smirked at the idea realizing how many holes his concept might have and empowered by a new wave of doubt wrote down a note to himself, which stuck to the wall, participates in his daily life until today 'he who does not doubt, does not want to know'.

II.   What is normal for the spider, can be madness for the fly…

The idea of different points of view and a variety of opinions on each topic, dilemma, and discourse appears to be a constant, non-changing part of this experience we call *life*. When being presented with any information, notice, or opinion, everyone's mind subconsciously processes new input and presents a biased, first-hand resolution to the thinker. As the answer occurs quickly, in a matter of seconds, our mind has an already prepared solution and opinion, based on its qualities and experience. This is not to say, that these first-hand projections are anywhere near the true, genuine, and prospective outcome. They are merely expressions of our small mind, whose constant analysing and decision making happens outside our conscious thoughts and can be considered quite a distraction.

*

When (if) we give in to the suggestions which our small mind has produced, over a brief period, we are at risk of losing control of how our reaction to the presented situation turns out. The prospective thinking, in this case, would be that of a conscious, disciplined mind, whose awareness of its flaws lets the thought and reaction hang in the void between the stimuli and response for a little longer before being acted upon. That brief space in time holds the key to the control and self-care of the thinker. As Victor Frankl states *'in our response lies our growth and our freedom.'* Without giving in to the conditioned, mind-driven reactions, the decision on how to react has a greater chance of being made; and when made consciously can bring a better understanding to the nature of an individual's existence and their subconscious preconceived expectations, and opinions. As the creatures of habit humans have let their habitual behaviour override more and more areas of life, which when taken into auto-mode, become futile, and prone to suffering. This lack of consciousness within our daily lives can lead to a prolonged feeling of misery, disappointment, and overall lack of satisfaction with the life lived. It is as if through letting ourselves think less (conscious thinking), we leave more space for thinking (subconscious thinking) with our conditioned egotistical minds. This shift of responsibilities can at first seem quite comforting. We do not have to think that much anymore, as the thinking takes care of itself, but the more we surrender this selective thinking to our subconscious, small-minded, survival-driven ego, we become the prisoners of our conditioned own mind. This change, sometimes out of laziness, apathy, or just lack of notice (mindless living) can shortly become a major issue within the daily life of an individual, as every new input must be diagnosed and decided upon through the filter of the ego.

To reclaim our mindful freedom, we are obliged to take care of our mind; again, and again discerning the false fears, ideas, and conditioned thought processes; and once connected with the voice within recognize that there is no such thing which is either this or that and nothing else. Thanks to this lack of acceptance to what (specifically) that thing is, we can arrive at a stance of more discourse, open-minded decision making, and clarity, through which each statement, news information, and opinion can be decided upon from the higher self, taking into account our flaw-full mind.

III.   *Isn't it true that each word, action, or point of view can be reframed and assigned to its counterpart...?*

The boy pondered on the idea of selfishness and selflessness following the discussion he had a chance to experience the day before. During the resilience workshop, one of the participants pointed out that *taking care of thyself can become selfish when the wellbeing of ours is put forward as the highest priority. On the other hand,* he argued, *being selfless brings about the wellbeing of thyself with it.* The boy considered his point of view and agreed to an extent. *Yes,* he thought, *we do have to be a little selfish to put ourselves first, but being too selfless can bring about as much harm as extreme selfishness...* It felt like a great subject to navigate the mind with, therefore he decided to put it into thinking practice and went about his evening contemplating the difference between the two, weighing all the pros and cons of both.

*

Sitting down to his night-time routine of writing and recording, he scribbled a note on a piece of paper, which he earlier used as the shopping list. *Selfish vs selfless* the note announced. Looking at the two contradictories, he got to his writing and freed his awareness from the constant spinning and rinsing of the discussion's topic. After a while, his hand suddenly slipped off the keyboard and picking up the pencil, added a little sentence beneath selfish, *when helping another you need to take care for your safety first – first aid.* The boy looked at the noted phrase and remembered the training, he used to pass yearly to validate his qualifications. *That is very true* he admitted, *the first step to save another was always to take care of your safety, otherwise, I couldn't help...* He imagined the kind of situation, in which the rescuer forgets to look left and right before running out on the road or steps into the paddle of electricity-charged water because of the forgetfulness in regard to that first point and made out a smile.

He realized what the whole discussion, that they've been through earlier, was missing. *I cannot help if I am not able to,* he concluded, *for example, because I would be hit by another car while trying to reach the victim who had the accident in the middle of the highway...*

*

Leaving the recording material on the side, the boy picked up his notebook and wrote down his thoughts regarding that 'positive' selfishness, instantly realizing that if there is the second side to this coin, there must be an opposite approach to the idea of selflessness as well. Recalling the times, when concerning others, he would put his plans, opinions, or wishes down, he realized the truth about being selfless. *Sometimes being selfless can harm our life* he recited his thoughts, *as well as sometimes being selfish can save it...* In awe of the discovery, so simple yet so profound, he revised his daily routines and decisions made in the past, considering which ones of them could be seen as selfless and which as selfish acts. He remembered the times he would abandon his plans to stay home, read, or just relax, in pursuit of acknowledgment and acceptance of his friends, with whom he would end up drinking, smoking, and ultimately doing himself more harm than good. A selfless act, which was causing him trouble. He shook his head acceptant of the past, nevertheless slightly disappointed with his younger self. He thought of the times when because of feeling the guilt, arising from the idea of selfishness, he would go out partying with his girlfriend even though all he wished for was to stay inside and watch a movie, and vice versa: being drawn towards the dancefloor night, when his loved one *didn't feel like it and would rather stay home. Don't we all sometimes make these mistakes* he reassured his consciousness, *sometimes out of selfish guilt, sometimes out of selfless pressure...?*

*

The boy was certain his thinking had a seed of truth within. Considering the things, he chose to do throughout his days that could be considered selfish, which were mostly those that made him grow, become better, and ultimately become more of a selfless person. He recognized that a joyful, satisfied human being; one that could be pointed out as a selfish one if considered through their routine and the amount of time they spent doing their 'thing', was the best person to become selfless and share their joy and satisfaction of life with others. *Isn't it that those who do not appreciate others that struggle to appreciate themselves...?* He pondered on the idea, trying to find reasons for it to be awfully wrong or completely right, and concluded that there is no black and white.

Life just isn't that simple. *It's all slightly shaded* he smirked, imagining the world seen through the eyes of a dog or a cat, as he remembered to have heard once, that either of these species sees the world in a rather grey palette of colours. *It's not either-or with things* he thought, *there are too many layers for it all to be as simple as that...* He considered his self-care, and self-love, which practiced everyday gave him a sense of fulfilment and purpose, as well as provided his body and mind with something to lean on, whenever the seas of life became stormy and rough. His conclusion steamed through his brain, gained through awareness and self-reflection, *to be truly, positively selfless you have to have integrity* he wrote *and to have integrity you have to be selfish at times and take care of your wellbeing first. You cannot save another if you're going to hurt yourself before carrying out the act of help...*

ADRESSED TO ALL

I. *Some of us prefer to sit underneath the blanket, while others would rather get up and turn the heating up instead... These differences of approach are what makes us who we are...*

The day was chilly, one of a kind which announces its sunrise with a mist of frosting covering the window glass. The boy got up as per usual, at seven, and sitting down to his morning writing tried to digest the thoughts and ideas that his discussion with a friend brought upon the plane of consideration the day before. Their conversation took quite a while; over two hours to be more specific, and meandered among subjects of all kinds, coming back to one pervasive theme every now and then; that of a difference in approaches to life. His good friend from back home has been struggling a little lately with his other half and as it usually happens, the boy could easily relate, as he also found such a situation daily trouble of his existence. He might have not been with the girl exactly at the time, but the thoughts and memories of these issues were very much so fresh and vivid to his young mind. They chatted away, each in their environment, one strolling down the seafront with a cup of take-away coffee, the other marching around his own flat's living room while waiting for his father to drop off a few things. It was a pleasurable talk and one of those, which enable the minds to collide and create solutions and ideas unable to grasp with only one set of thinking process involved. *It's good to brainstorm* the boy thought recollecting the way their conversation happened, *it refreshes your mind loads...*

*

His friend at some point came up with a great representation of the difference in the attitude of his own and his girl, which seemed to be the case for the boy's experience as well. *It's like trying to deal with a temperature in the house* his friend explained, *some of us would rather just put the blanket on and stay underneath it... Others would rather take action and change the radiator's settings* he continued, *I think this is a fair representation of the case, to be honest.* The boy nodded his head, remembering the concept and writing his thoughts down, noted additional few words below the quote *you cannot take either of these approaches too far* and quickly remembered the follow-up on the conversation, which ironically represented just that. *But you know* his friend would say, *if you stay too long under the blanket it's no good... neither is too constantly walking to change the settings...* Both chuckled heartily for the thought of the extremes.

One can get you frozen underneath the blanket, the other tired out and without time to do anything else concluded the boy, his approval for his friend's idea hearable in the deep echo of the laugh within. It was a great way of perceiving their situation and the boy considered the theme as quite a funny one as well. It makes sense he agreed, nodding his head while writing down the memorized phrase. Trying to figure out how to address this aspect of human nature and the idea of being with one another, when the difference in approaches is so visible, he leaned back on his chair and looked outside for a moment. *It's not easy to shift your perspective* he pondered, *even more so to understand the perspective of another...* Wobbling from side to side on his desk seat, he tapped the fingers against the counter and tried to see the bigger picture of the whole idea. *How to live with that other half without abandoning your approach* he wondered. The concept of this metaphor was based upon the fact that one of the two wanted to travel and explore, while the other was acting out the will to stay and settle for what was already theirs. The boy's friend struggled a little to find the right way to deal with the situation. He didn't want to lose the girl at the same time attempting to make her feel empowered to pursue the desires, she had in mind. The boy, who recognized many similarities to his personal experience with a certain girl of his, empathized with his mate and actively engaging in the conversation provided his point of view, at the same time thoroughly listening to what his friend had to say. After all, the conversation can only work if understanding comes before communicating. Their ideas and approaches varied, but the honest wish to help one another made their brainstorming worthy and quite tiring to the mind. Nevertheless, it was a great eye-opener for the boy as well as his friend. *It's a great way to shift your perspective bro* his friend pointed out at some point at the later time of their conversation, *a really useful chat...* They both agreed on this fact for sure.

*

The discussion coming to an end, after multiple layers of conversation, a rather extreme number of side-themes, and plenty of laughs, the two finished their chat, getting back to their daily chores. *It was never a goal to come up with a solution anyway* the boy thought, recollecting the stories and thoughts shared, *after all, there is no 'one size fits all' when it comes to life and especially relationships in life...* Their conversation was golden in the boy's opinion; therefore, he decided to commemorate it and write it down. His friend, happy with the new perspective, went on to tackle his case. The boy did the same. *Wonder what we are going to share next time* the boy thought; *if we all thought the same and saw the world the same, wouldn't it be a bit boring...?*

II. You claim you would die for your country, but you hate your fellow countryman for their taste in clothing...

The boy was sat in front of the TV with his family. The election night was long gone, a few days passed, and the news showed yet another gathering of the right-wing supporters, who in all their love for the country heaved with hate for those who do not look, sound, or dress like them. *How does one hold so much hate to another human being* the boy pondered, trying to make some sort of sense out of all that happened recently. He felt ashamed and angry, tired of all the negativity that surrounded his country for centuries only to arrive at this place of even a lower point of 'civility'. *One would think we are the 1st world country* he said with a sour taste gathering at the back of his throat, as he felt the painful range of emotions arising, *how did we get here...?* The boy wasn't only an observer anymore. He has taken part in the voting, argued about different campaign programs, and with more and more awareness made his choices coming back to the urn every 4 years with the hope of seeing the change for the better, only to discover it is going to get worse...

*

Since the boy moved out of the country a few years back, many changes in his life happened. He met new kinds of situations, was shown a different point of view, made friends with people of all colours, orientation, interests, and coming from all kinds of backgrounds, with each encounter enriching his rather scarce view on the world. His body changed, slowly arriving at its prime state in which he was going to see it only deteriorate with age, reaching its peak in the next couple of years. He felt great with life around him, seeing how well one can live among all others, not necessarily aggreging with everything that happens but accepting that which is not his freedom to choose. *The freedom of one ends where the freedom of another begins,* he quoted Tocqueville whenever his point of view did not meet the agreement with his friends' opinion, making it possible to live with each other regardless of the differences. This sentence quoted during one of the lessons in his early adolescence gave him a great deal of understanding to others and with time became his motto, whenever his conscience wouldn't agree with what his friends or family were up to. The boy believed that through the acceptance and non-judgment to one another, everyone can live happily and at peace with all, and if their actions did not intrude on someone else's health, state of being, or property it was only fair to let them do as they please. *Everyone is their own self and there is no right or wrong in that which affects only the person taking the action* he reminded himself, whenever one of his close mates chose something that seemed destructive or negative for their wellbeing.

His belief went a long way, with tolerance to all actions, regardless of their nature and possible outcomes. *I might caution you not to touch the burning log* the boy said once to his friend, *but I will not forbid you to, as it is your hand and your right to burn it accordingly.* With all this in mind, he came back and forth to his country of origin learning about the state of affairs each time he crossed the border, meeting his motherland for another 'vacation' time.

*

Years passed, the new laws were made and as the boy crossed the border again, he shortly discovered a major change happening within his beloved country. The government with its obsessive imposition of morals and ideas became a bully, each day promoting more and more negativity and spreading hate across the social groups of all ages, making it almost impossible for the citizens to live at peace with one another. *What has changed* the boy pondered, *where all this despise comes from...* As he knew from history lessons, books, and stories of the days passed, there was always a place for discrimination and hate whenever the fear of 'otherness' overweighed the love to fellow man, and with the radical (populist) party in power for the past years, spreading misinformation, manipulating media, and fuelling the rage within the hearts of those who do not think much for themselves, the animosity within the society grew. *Power is addictive* the boy reminded himself, as he saw the program proposed by the populist party, which took over the country for the past years and seemed very unlikely to surrender their position at this point. With more and more people 'waking up' to see what is happening with their motherland, which a few years back was on the prominent way to join the union of the continent in the race to civility and harmony, they felt the need for change. The voices of hope arose and each day closer to the voting time the chance for improvement grew, but the party in power did not want to leave the office easily, playing on more and more emotionally driven chords in order to keep the power to themselves, manipulating the people whose biggest worries of the day were which TV channel to watch or when to meet for another round of drinking. The division grew as the day of voting closed. The chances were high, but were they ever high enough...?

*

With the election night coming closer, the populist party needed more confidence, more certainty of the success, which drew on promoting hate and fear rather than hope and love among their potential electors.

With only a few weeks to go, their manifesto of negativity was brought to life, spreading hate among all those who have never seen another way of living before. Drawing on their 'high morals of religion and patriotic chords' the party in power proposed a new way of discriminating those who do not fit the archaic, medieval portray of a family, which can be only dated back to the times when electricity was not even a dream and people died of disease on the streets on the daily basis. With national media under their belt and the vicious power of the institution of church advertising for their cause, the populist party grew stronger led by the men whose opinion of the world and the moral spine could be summarised in the word 'fear' and 'complexes', who chose their line of the campaign aimed at those who live poorly, do not educate themselves much and spend their time on a socially sourced funds in front of the nation led television. Sadly, enough the campaign of hate worked and the hope for change started to decline.

*

The boy pondered on the situation, which caused him a great deal of grief, leaving his heart hurt and his mind uneasy. Trying to understand how does one, like those in power, manages to gain it in such a malicious way, with only negativity to spread and animosity to grow. His voice broke, as he continued to discuss the possible future for the country he once left, the one he once wanted to go back to, wondering what kind of situation he will arrive at in the years to come. Knowing how much it takes to take down the tyrants, the bullies, and the haters of this world, he hoped one day his countrymen will manage and with love rather than hate, the world around his house will become a more welcoming one. He sat down on the pavement in front of his house, reminiscing of the history, which 'likes to repeat itself' and once more seemed to be shouting in his ears *'I'm back!'*. Always interested in the past, he recognized a huge similarity in the way their country was led nowadays, with the way and approach parties like NSDAP or CPSU, which used their manipulative abilities, national resources, and the speech of hate to divide and conquer not only their own but also the countries nearby. As he pondered on the fate, which once more seemed to be dawning on his beloved, mistreated by history country, he felt the pinch of agitation gathering at the back of his spine. *The time for change will come, one way or another* he heard his mind-manifesting the hopeful truth, *maybe not today, maybe not tomorrow, but it will.*
Where there is hope, there is a way…

WHO WERE, ARE, AND WILL BE

I.   *Whether you believe in coincidence or not, whether you think*
        everything happens for a reason, there are moments in life,
        which become surprisingly powerful and alter the flow of one's
        existence… and more likely than not, they happen all the time…

The boy was about to throw the ball, aiming at one of his friends. They
were on the beach and the game, which he remembered from his childhood
drew the attention of a few friends, who joined in to see it through. The
rules were fairly easy and all of them got the gist of it quickly. The sun was
slowly coming down the horizon as they continued the game. In the middle
of the beach, a big circle was drawn using the boy's feet and divided into a
few parts it was supposed to resemble Earth. Each player owned a piece of
land and through throwing and avoiding the ball, they were to take each
other's terrain. Whoever was the last one standing or owning the most land
at the end of the game, was to be the winner. The boy enjoyed the game,
seeing the sparkling eyes of his colleagues, who were having fun with it as
well.

*

The boy remembered the game from his early youth. Suddenly realizing it
was once played, he offered his friends a go at it and was very happy to
have the chance to play it once more. Standing in that circle, sipping beer
from a bottle, which got a little sand all over the top, he reminisced about
the time in his past, when he played it ferociously with his cousins and
siblings. It was one of the games that caused a lot of drama, he was certain
of that. *Which game doesn't at such a young age* he thought shortly after,
reasoning with the memories from his youth. Images of moments, when he
used to play it outside his summer house, drew him closer to his younger
self. He remembered the way his older cousin used to take all his country
surface in one go, because of his long arms and when his sister would throw
the ball a little too weak giving him a chance to take some of her territories.
It was a great game he pondered, *one of many*. Thinking of all the time that
passed, he continued indulging in this entertainment from his youth, which
somehow, by a little luck and his memory, crept into today's fun on the
beach with friends, at the age of twenty-three. *We are still young* he
thought.

*

At some point during the game, an older man walked past them and
stopped, looking at their running, throwing, and drawing on the sand.

He stood there for a while, his backpack hanging off his shoulders. His hair was grey, covered with a bucket hat, his beard signifying the age himself. He held the backpack with his hands, sandals dangling on the sides of the bag. The boy noticed the man and smiled at him, once the next round was about to start. The man shuffled in his spot and seemed to gather himself to say something. The boy left the ball in the middle of the drawn map and the round was about to start when the old man's voice reached their ears. *You made me remember when I was that small,* he said, putting his hand close to his knees, smile written on his face, *thank you...* The boy looked at him, heart-filling out with warmth, and approached the man. *That's amazing sir* he said. *What was it called* the man pondered, *pinko... pirko...? Piwko* the boy answered, *czarne piwko naprzeciwko wywołuje...* He recited a little verse, that participated in the starting of each round. The man's eyes sparkled as he seemed to remember even more. A small tear danced in the corner of the man's eye for a moment. *Piwko* he said, *yes... yes, I do remember now...* The boy felt how powerful the moment must have been for the man. He smiled at him and nodded his head; *hope you have a great day sir!* The man nodded his head, about to continue his walk along the beach, *you made me remember my early youth, thank you, thank you so much...!* He walked away, taking small steps in the sand. The boy observed the man, thinking of the time that passes so quickly and unnoticeably for all. It was amazing to feel what he felt, seeing the man's eyes brighten for the remembrance of the days passed such a long time ago. He didn't believe in coincidence and thankful for this humbling experience, he went back to the game, thinking of the amazing power of the situation he experienced. His eyes were still a little moist as they started the next round. *That's crazy* he thought, *truly amazing...*

II.   *Time stops for no one...*

The boy was struggling to keep his balance, as the boxes on his shoulders waved from side to side. He was walking up the stairs, helping his friend to move into his new apartment. As excited as they both were, now they resembled a pair of red-faced tomatoes dressed in their casual clothing. The flat was on the top floor and the struggle up the stairs was certainly one that did not offer too much comfort for the body. Reaching the top, the boy strained his strength to put the boxes softly on the floor and stood by the wall breathing heavily. *That is the last one* his friend exclaimed, shuffling the boxes with his foot as he made his way to the door. The boy nodded and still catching breath, looked around the staircase filled with boxes, bags, and items of different nature. They went into the flat and one by one, shuffled all belongings into the living room.

The boy stood in the middle, smiling as he saw the satisfaction and excitement written on his friend's face. *He always dreamt of moving out* he thought, *good for him…* They sat down on the sofa, which creaked with a loud noise, noticing their arrival, and felt their tensed bodies relax. The boy looked around the room, scanning the space in which his friend was about to start a new chapter of his life. They have been here before, as this flat used to belong to one of their older friends, a while ago. *Like a déjà vu* the boy pondered. As if his friend heard his thoughts, he turned to face him and made a joke waving his hand expressively, *isn't it funny that Wojtek used to live here?!* The boy smiled, nodding the head in approval, *yeah, it's a bit mad if you ask me… Imagine* the boy continued, *time stops for no one, yet this flat seems frozen in it…*

*

His friend kept unpacking, as the boy sipped coke, which was granted to him for the effort and help he has given. Satisfied with a moment of rest, he observed his friend's decisive moments of where and what to put, which reminded him of his removals, when everything seems fresh and new, heaving with potential and excitement of change. *Sometimes change can be exciting* he pondered, *sometimes though it can be scary…* He thought of his situation. Days of the summer were nearing the end and it was soon time to depart back to where his work and everyday life resided. *Across the sea I go,* he murmured a little sad of the ending so quickly arriving at its final summer station. Reminding himself of the new flat he also has rented recently, the spirit within him raised from its seat, *that's going to be exciting…* He smiled at his thoughts, leaving those of sorrow and longing on the side, *no time for you just yet.* His years looked similar for the past few. He would visit his hometown occasionally, spent some time with family and friends, and depart soon after to continue his education, work-life, and social life outside of their sight. Usually, it dawned on him on the day of the travel but this time it was different, as he recognized how much he missed time like this one in the company of his friends. This summer was special and through its uniqueness, it became tough to leave behind. He pondered on the subject, while the coke in the glass bubbled up and out, becoming more and more 'flat'.

*

A few moments passed as the boy sat on the sofa, letting his mind wander back and forth, noticing nothing outside his consciousness, while his friend finished unpacking the essentials. *I will have to get him some sort of house gift* the boy thought, *a housewarming present they call it…*

His friend threw the last big bag into the bin on the side and sat in the armchair, satisfied with his work. *Man,* he exclaimed, *I am so happy!* The boy could see it regardless of the words. He nodded acknowledging his friend's happiness. Thank you so much for your help bro his friend continued, I was so excited to do this, my work from home today was close to none… He laughed briefly. I love moving houses the boy answered, it feels… refreshing… Silent agreement filled the room. His friend's eyes sparkled with happiness. What a time to be alive he said, what a time…! The boy smiled amazed with the pureness of the emotions his friend was presenting. He knew it meant the world to him to move out of his parents' flat, but now, in the midst of it all, he was able to notice the pure joy that radiated from his friend's satisfaction. Amazing the boy thought, just awesome…

*

They sat in the living room for a while, sipping their drinks and talking about the time they both had during this summer. Both worked from home, which meant 'no days off', even though most of the days seemed like days free from work. *It is different to work from home* the boy thought, *feels less work-like…* They chatted away, considering the times passed and looking into the glimpses of their dreamt future. The boy felt happy with how it all turned out. *It's an exciting time* he said, *for you to finally be on your ground…* He waved his hand, underlining the statement. His friend nodded ecstatically. *It's like a dream coming true* he answered, *hundred percent…!* They pondered for a moment. *Isn't it crazy how flats and houses last generation, while people within them grow old and die* the boy stated, noticing the impermanence of it all, *it's like they are not alive, but manage to outlive us all…* His friend smirked. *You always have to think so deeply my man* he laughed, *I guess that's just your thing nowadays…* They laughed briefly. The boy knew his friend accepted his weirdness anyway. *I am just wondering* he continued, *how many other people lived in this flat before you… and how many will live after…* His friend looked around the room, his eyes squinting slightly as he tried to imagine the number of years this building had under his belt. *That's a good question my friend* he said, *I bet more than we would think of…* They sat together pondering, seeing the time fly underneath their feet as their years came and went. They were adults already but felt far from it. *How long does one live until they realize the longevity of their existence…?*

III. *Little kids are very much so like tiny people, whose voice has been taken away for the unknown purpose of some wicked experiment... or maybe they just know too much to even bother speaking...*

The boy was standing behind his friend, as they waited for the door to open. They were visiting his friend's sister, who to the boy's amazement had a two-year-old kid. Just the kind of kid everyone wants to play with for some time, but no-one would want to be taking care of for more than half a day. They waited for the doorbell to ring out its tune and as the footsteps approached, the door opened with a little and a normal-sized head peeking out. We're here his friend concluded, opening his arms towards the little one, who in amazement looked up at the two, who has arrived at his castle's doorstep. *I wonder if little kids like him consider the door to be one or is it more of a teleportation machine of some sort, which amazes each time someone answers it* the boy pondered, as they entered the flat and settled on the patio outside. The little one was always very much so interested in everything, constantly shifting its point of interest, like a little puppy whose focus shifts every moment. Sitting around the patio, everyone observed the main star of the event, the little boy, who seemed to the boy like a tiny person, whose voice has been taken away. Making a few sounds at a time, he appeared to understand everything, just struggling to communicate anything back. The boy thought about the idea, which seemed to dawn on him as he observed the activities of this tiny human. *Maybe he just doesn't bother to speak* he thought, *maybe it is just because of lacking motivation to speak anything at all. What's the point* he pondered, *maybe they just know something we don't as being those older ones, whose egos takes place, steps in, and ultimately overwhelms the little child within.* The little one took his uncle's glasses and played with them, putting on his face upside down and giggling intensively. *The other way around, honey* his mother advised, but the communication flowed right through his ears. *No need for a change* the boy pondered, *maybe he just knows better or thinks he knows best.* Smiling to the little one, everyone continued their conversation, as the little child always continued to find new ways of playing. The boy considered the freedom, which tiny humans seem to have in connection to any activity whatsoever. *As fragile as they are, they might be the best potential criminals, considering no one would take their actions seriously* he concluded, smiling in amusement as the thought arose. *Sometimes I wish I could go back to this free state of mind* he pondered, *one day I just might do so...*

THINKING

'To find yourself, think for yourself.'

~ Socrates

ABOUT THINKING

I.   *The same way the rain falls upon the Earth, clouds stopping the Sun from its mighty shine, our emotions and thoughts can overwhelm the inner greatness of ourselves. It is in our capacity and control to choose however we will react to this weather and whether we allow these constant rain of thoughts and feelings to influence our state of Being...*

The drops of soaking, refreshing rain tapped on the window outside the house of the boy. Sat in the cross-legged position in front of his laptop he tapped away the sentences onto the page. His fingers danced between the buttons, letters creating the words staining the screen with their magical quality of storytelling. *What a day* he thought, looking outside the glassed frame, *better to stay inside, I guess...* There isn't usually much to be done on Sundays anyway, most of the people spending their free days with their loved ones and engaging in the activities of their heart's choice. It was similar for the boy, the only difference being he wasn't with his loved ones at the time. They were far away from him, living their life back home, which in his mind painted a beautiful, colourful landscape of memories and sentiments. There was the inner voice, which cried to them whenever he reminded himself of the qualities his family inspired within him. *I miss you and I love you* he exclaimed, letting the words fill the void of emotions that seemed to stutter the quiet commands inside his mind, *I will see you soon.* He straightened his back and listened to the quiet rainy concert. He thought of the Sun, which always present, at the time seemed absent, yet so obviously only hidden behind the soft, woven sea of clouds covering the sky. *I like the rain* he concluded and smiling within he continued his morning routine, which worked as a metaphorical and practical therapy for his soul.

*

Rivers of little droplets running down the window's glass meandered streaming towards the ground. His mind similar to the rain in its might and constant flow subjected his thoughts to the never-ending concert of arising thoughts and feelings, emotional dance within. There was an unsung beauty in this process of recognizing and letting go of the noticed experientially ideas, which grew within to become life just for a tiny term of the moment, only to be flushed away with the new ones arising. The note board above his desk announced the tasks to be fulfilled, continuity of his life secured by these simple attributes of assistance. He looked at the board for a moment, learning what was that his past Self required of him at this time.

There wasn't anything that couldn't wait until the weekday and following the idea of relaxing throughout the weekend, he decided to not act upon them for now. The wish to explore the avenues of creativity strong as ever motivated his actions for the day. His desire to write was the one keeping him sleepless at night. Imagination at those times of silence and closeness to the inner voice inspired him to wander the fields of possible futures and dreams that might or might not come true one day. He felt at peace with it, similarly to the perception of a rainy day is only a moment in the constantly unfolding eternity of time. *If only everyone would see the world the way I see it sometimes* he thought, *it might bring peace to those who suffer as well.* He pondered on the idea of how much influence we let the thoughts have over ourselves when without notice we surrender our perception of happiness to the flowing rain of feelings and emotions. Knowing that there is no possible way of turning the thought-chatter off, he recognized that the 'free will' granted to the conscious beings is what makes the option of separating oneself from this inner noise only if the thinker decides to do so. *You are not your thoughts* he remembered the sentence from one of the pieces of writing he encountered during the many hours spent over different books of great philosophers and writers. It gave him the feeling of ease, whenever what his mind experienced didn't feel right to the awareness within. Looking down at the street below his window he observed the paddles of water forming here and there, the drops of rain constantly adding to their size and shape, tapping the rings of ripples, which echoed throughout the surface. The beauty of the phenomenon stroked his senses and imagining himself as a pool of liquid light he concerned the thoughts to work similarly, tapping away their little stories on the flat, flowing surface of the soul, their rippling effect arising and quickly, in a matter of seconds, dissolving into the vessel of life he was.

*

His awareness of the daily habits he has unconsciously and consciously programmed within his being enabled him to see a little clearer how the world perceived through his eyes is. There were things he despised and looking into the nature of this emotion he recognized the reasons for such reaction to them. Some experiences just didn't resonate with his heart the way one would want to receive them. Living in the time when everything happened instantly, by the click of a button, he savoured the moments of inner peace, which at times were so scarce for the taking.

Other experiences made a big impact on the vessel of his heart, seeing the reason for their existence as purely pleasurable to his senses and inner voice, which quietened at those times of perfect synchronicity seemed to manifest itself more vividly than ever. Meditation perceived by him as the best tool in accessing this deeper level of existence helped a lot. He tried it for some time and now, after months of practice, he didn't feel like stopping, if anything wishing to do more and more of it in the days to come. It allowed his mind to settle and accept the things as they are, regardless of the emotional baggage that the events in his life carried towards him. Like a rain tapping away on the surface of the pavement, his thoughts tapped away on the roof of his heart, only to slip down and away as the serenity of practice prevailed. *It's all in the mind* he reminded himself of a phrase from the Beatles movie, which made such a great impression on him a while ago, *the way we perceive what happens is the source of both joy and suffering. It is up to us which we choose to accept and take in at the time* he concluded.

II.   *Sensing his body emptying, he felt like levitating just above his bedroom carpet, which suddenly felt so different, after all these years of its presence...*

The boy's breath was deep and slow. His chest flowed up and down with the waves of the air filling up the lungs. He was close to a sleeping state, yet his mind was more alert than usual, keeping the experience on a purely sensational level. His eyes closed and his body spilled on the surface of the carpet, he took a deep inhale and focused on the top of his head. *How does it feel there* he thought, moving his awareness slowly down the head, *how does it feel here...?* Similarly, to a laser or an x-ray scan, his mind moved down the body, stopping on each part for just a moment, to feel into its sensation and, in a manner without judgment, relieve any stress from each place. Listening experientially to the vessel which carried his spirit, he felt his form disappearing into abys more and more, with each part surrendered to the technique. Leaving what now seemed only a pulp of shapeless matter, energized yet quietened with the months of daily practice, he reached the tips of his toes and finalized the 'scan', letting his mind observe his earthly form as one. The sensation of levitating came to his senses soon after the ending. Letting himself be still, his eyes closed, his mind calmed, his breath slow and settled, he became aware of the lack of feelings, which were present with him just a moment ago. It seemed as if his body was no longer there, in the form which one would assume it to be, rather than as a free flowing, almost non-existent in the sense of physical feeling, mass. Having the sensation of levitating spread through his being, he felt his muscles relax a little deeper, as his mind settled into this place of inner quiet. Everything seemed to fade away, similarly to the feeling of falling asleep, yet his mind, as alert as it was, presently recognized and reacted to the situation, giving the boy a soft nudge of mindfulness, which trained with time and associated with the control of the breathing, offered an active awareness of the moments similar to the one experiencing right now.

*

Whenever I feel this relaxation, everything done before seems lacking in the importance he pondered, as if something present with me for all this time, was hidden in the plain sight... The boy was still on the floor, his body sinking deeper into the surface, as his mind wandered. Reactivity subsided, giving space to the conscious discussion within. He considered the opportunities connected with such activities as the one, he was presently experiencing. It does calm the mind a little he thought revising his own perspective and approach to things and occurrences within his life since his practice began.

Can be a little tricky though his mind added, to which he admitted a fair deal of truthfulness, *but what isn't challenging at the beginning...?* Bouncing back off the initial point, his mind seemed to have the discussion under control, more constructive than many the boy has had a chance to participate in before. *In all honesty, though, it has helped me loads* he made the effort of expressing his opinion within, adding to the ongoing discourse. *Look how calm I can be nowadays* he added as if underpinning his previous point and hopefully finishing the subject. He took a deep breath, briefly taking control over the mind's focus and shifting it onto the sensation of inhalation, rather than continuing the conversation within. The chest puffed up, making the mind feel as if its vessel of a body was about to burst like an inflated balloon, quickly dissipating down as the breath went away. The boy softly wiggled his toes, waking up the corpse, in which his consciousness resided. The levitating sensation gradually gave way to the growing awareness of the shape, density, and size of the body. *Feels like waking up to the life* he thought, *or like being reborn again... Not that I know how that feels though* he chuckled within. His lips joined the spirit in a smile following the thought and as he fluttered his eyes open, his mind finally awakened fully.

*

Realizing the way, his being feels sometimes, especially through meditation and those brief moments of full awareness, the boy recognized the difference between how he has considered himself before the whole adventure of inner inquiry. Slowly and gently bringing himself to seated he reminisced about the way he perceived reality a few years back and surprisingly to his mind, realized that most of the actions and situations he has taken part in were merely a reaction to the outside world, without any control over the reactions themselves. *It almost feels like I've been running on autopilot* he concluded, shifting his weight to the right and pushing the surface of the ground away from himself, letting his vessel raise and stand tall within the space, which he called home for so many years. He looked at the carpet, remembering many different occasions which the carpet must have remembered, and considered the way this piece of the material felt a moment ago when sunken in the state of non-shape his body rested on its surface. *Felt like a different carpet then,* the boy pondered. He approached the door and swinging it open to start a day recognized a thought, which flashed within his freshly awakened mind. *Feels like a different body as well...*

III. The life energy of one expands with the presence of another…

The boy was sat cross-legged in the middle of a fairly sized hall, his gaze soft and breath slowly expanding the chest as he breathed. Space was filled with people of all ages sitting in different positions, scattered on the mats at a similar distance to one another. The centre of the hall was marked by an oversized, golden monument of a sitting Buddha, garmented with flowers by its feet. The crown of the statue was black, with two items held in the crossed arms in front of the sculpture. A few smaller ornaments accompanied the sitting statue, set in perfect harmony of space and size across the small table. The red garment, which covered the surface of the furniture signalled the sacredness of the items placed on it. Above the statue, a few different portrays were visible. Presenting both monks and founders of this Buddhism shelter the pictures drew attention to the genuine smiles and sparkling eyes of the portrayed. The boy observed the surroundings with a bit of scepticism, reminding himself that there is no one perfect, only way to pray, meditate and practice spirituality and therefore any idolization of anyone or anything other than the path to revelation itself should be disregarded on the base of being false in its faultiness. *Nothing is separate, everything is connected* the boy reminded himself of the wisdom the books of different philosophies taught him. Looking at his friend next to him, he felt the happiness arising. He was proud they came. Sometimes the hardest aspect of trying a new experience is to get yourself to do it and knowing his friend's opinions about spirituality, he was satisfied with the pure fact of presence in the place. *Wisdom through experience* he recalled the empiric truths, represented by a few in the past, and knowing that there is no such thing as a bad attempt, he came to the centre with an open mind and hopeful heart. The man, who appeared to play the role of the leader during today's session sat down next to a small, knee-high table and opened a little booklet, which must have been the instruction or a program of the celebration. People who arrived a little late spilled into the hall and quickly, in a quiet manner took their mats and chosen the last free spaces to rest, preparing for the meditation. The boy looked towards the monument once more, trying to remember as many details of it as possible, before his eyes would shut, as the leader exclaimed his wish to welcome all newcomers and those who practice for some time already and opened the little booklet, giving a sign for participants to relax and close their eyes.

*

The session began. The boy closed his eyes softly and focused on his breath, listening to the words of the man with the book. With a few words of introduction, time for settling into the peaceful space has started

Breathing in, the boy listened to the air rushing through his nostrils, down the throat, and into the lungs, expanding the chest even more as it went. With the breath out, he felt the flattening of the chest and pressure building up within his belly. Time slowed as the breaths were all he focused on, his train of thoughts passing by without stopping. The boy knew a little about meditation already and reminding himself that there is no such thing as a mind free of any thoughts, he observed the ideas as they arose and disappeared into the ocean of his mind, feeling into the breath as the anchor for all attention. The initial part of 'settling in' lasted long enough for him to feel completely loose in his muscles, as the sensations of the body started to disappear from the frame of the conscious mind. The boy couldn't feel which arm was which anymore, his legs like a shapeless object hovering somewhere below his waist, his neck non-existent to the reception of the brain. This feeling of non-feeling relaxed him deeply, causing a rush of endorphins within the brain, making the pain at the bottom of his back diminish slightly. He always felt a little back pain while meditating and it's been a while until he accepted it as a part of the existence, not trying to change it by any means other than tending to his body. Alleviating the pain, he felt hovering on the matt in the room filled with quiet breathing noises all around.

IV.   *Thoughts in our mind remind me of a bird's erratic head twirls; they seem to constantly change direction…*

The boy was standing outside his flat, sipping on the hot coffee. Rain tapped against the pavement, splashing its drops all over the busy street. There was no sun to be seen, as the boy looked up at the sky and scanned the horizon with his gaze. *Gray day* he thought, *that's okay…* Leaning against the windowsill he noticed a blackbird sat on the chimney opposite his house. Giving it the attention, it deserved, he took a sip of the drink and thought of the ability to choose such a location for a morning rest. *Lucky you,* he murmured, as the bird rotated its head around without a stop, most likely in search for a company to join his chimney break, *maybe you're waiting for your date…?* Chuckling a little, considering whether this kind of pondering does not sound too absurd, the boy took a few steps towards the street and looked down the road scanning the roofs of the buildings. A few more chimneys and TV antennas were occupied. He noticed a few seagulls, another blackbird, and a crow, or at least some kind of a bird that reminded him of a crow. *Good morning everyone* he murmured, taking a step back and assuming the leaning position on the windowsill once more. He looked up, realizing that the neighbour has left his chimney already.

Oh, that's not nice is it he thought, without any goodbye...? Shaking his head, he entered the flat and closed the door, *not nice Mr. Bird... not nice.*

*

Taking a seat behind the desk, he left the coffee on the side and started typing. Unsure of the topic, which was to be discussed within his mind today, he decided to allow the palms to lead the way. *Sometimes this happens* he thought and reminding himself that there might be around sixty thousand thoughts a person has a day, he pondered on the absurdity, which emerged from lacking any initial idea for writing. *How can I not have any thought to write about then...?* Dumbfounded by the realization, he noticed that a few words are already coming into a sentence on the page, *thanks Muse*, he smiled. Looking out onto the street he wondered what the bird could have thought, when sat on the chimney he noticed the funny-looking boy down on the pavement. *Did you even notice me* he pondered *or were you too occupied with the search for another chimney to chill on...?* The boy laughed, the imagination of his proposing a silly landscape of chimneys with their space marked like the seats of a movie theatre, which only through reservation one could acquire. *What's with this monkey mind of mine today* he asked the space in front of his eyes, empowering the thoughts to wander even more. *It's a paradox* he contemplated, *the more you don't want to think of something, the more you do...*

*

Following this idea, he pondered on a way to present such a bold statement. *How to portray it* he raised the question, letting his brow raise its relaxed body as well. *Let's say* he started, *that I tell you to not think of a monkey, which is eating a banana right now...* The boy took a deep breath counting to five to let the future reader savour what has been said. *Now* he continued, *did you or did you not see the monkey eating a banana portrayed on the screen of your mind...? You did... I bet you did... I know I did.*

*

Laughing a moment, as his inner sight offered a somewhat out of the ordinary image of a banana-eating-monkey he scratched his cheek and thought of the words that would express this extraordinary phenomenon. *I think of it this way* he continued, *whenever we are told or tell ourselves to NOT think of something, our brain is already on it, by the time we want to overtake its gears with our conscious thoughts...*

The trick is to think what we WANT to think about, in order to get the brain working alongside rather than against us… Scanning through the sentences expressed, he wondered how many people out there consider this paradox to be one worth debating.

I bet all of us struggle with the thoughts sometimes he concluded pressing the 'coma' button on his keyboard.

*

He took a sip of coffee and allowed his thoughts to come back to the blackbird, Mr. Bird, if you will, whose presence, became such a big part of the morning world-contemplation. *What about yourself Mr. Bird* he asked silently, *do you struggle with the lack or overwhelm of thoughts at times…? If you do,* he added, *my advice for you is to start practicing meditation…* Turning on soft music, which mixed the air within his living room, he sat cross-legged on the floor and closed his eyes. *It helps to realize just how many thoughts you have throughout your day* he sent a mindful message across space, aiming it at the black bird's tiny head, *maybe it will help you as well… After all, you looked a little erratic turning your head as you did, on that chimney today…*

V.   The forest creaked softly in its eternal silence of existence. *You must be so lucky not having to think about all these things of the world*, the boy murmured looking at one of the trees. *What makes you think our static life excludes thinking* answered the tree.

The boy was sitting on top of a fallen tree trunk, dangling his feet from the edge. His forehead crunched and frowned, as he tried to come up with the topic to write about. *It's never easy when you want it too much* he noted with sour acceptance, *oh well…* Keeping his pen and paper close, he looked up and gazed at the wooden maze that surrounded him. He was somewhere in the middle of the forest, which has been a part of his hometown area for longer than he could probably imagine, and while enjoying the paths he found this secluded fallen tree clearing. The sun beamed between the leafless trunks occasionally, offering moments of serene warmth on one's skin. The boy observed the trees that quietly participated in this world of nature, which seemingly still natural, in many places was long exchanged for a synthetic, human-made one. He wished for the forests to stay the way they are. Reflecting on the beauty of nature surrounding him, he considered the eternal chatter his mind offered within, coming up with solutions, problems, ideas, and topics to analyse and often worry about without a moment to take a soothing breath. *That's the essence of consciousness* he pondered, *a constant avalanche of thought…*

Staring in the space covered by brown-shaded relics of life's essence, he heard a question arising between the many. One that was interesting enough to let it catch his attention for a moment – *do trees think...?* He pondered making out a silly smile as if his body was already promoting a response. *Surely thinking without being able to do anything would be rather daunting* he argued silently. He looked at the bark, which covered the trunk, on which he was sat, and scraping it with his nail quietly added – *although the saying 'to have the tough skin' could suggest otherwise... Maybe they're strong enough to not worry* he thought.

*

Jumping off the trunk, the boy picked up his pencil and notebook and walked towards the path. It was one less often used, for which he adored it. It felt almost sacred to be here, and he was there often. Sometimes when walking his dog, sometimes on his own, he appreciated coming around, sinking into the solitude of the forest, and letting his mind wander without distractions and commotion of the daily life out there, in the human world. He wasn't much of an introvert but recognized the natural need for quiet, which was so often overlooked by today's society. *There would be fewer mental health issues* he pondered *if more people would exercise the time on their own... Without the noise of the screen and scandalous civilization* he added. He passed by one of the trees and brushed its trunk with his hand. He stopped and keeping his hand on the trunk, closed his eyes. The forest creaked softly in its eternal silence of existence, as the boy listened. *You must be so lucky not having to think about all these things of the world* he murmured. *What makes you think our static life excludes thinking* answered the tree quietly. He smiled hearing the statement manifesting in his mind and imagined the forest as a huge tree convention. All the noises around him, all the creaks and rustle of the branches and trunks now reminded him of the chatter, small-talk, and heated discussion of the participants. The great conference of patience and courtesy. No one screams, no one talks over the other, everyone listens to understand. That is how the boy imagined the perfect world congress to act.
There is plenty we could learn from you he claimed opining his eyes *if only we would start to listen...*

ABOUT DOING

I.   *To become what one wishes for, the decision to let go of the current state and the being of the present needs to be committed... Like jumping off the roof into the darkness of the unknown, the belief of a net somewhere below being the only reassurance that everything will be as it should...*

The boy decided to make the first step. Now or never isn't it, he reassured himself poking the screen of his phone to confirm the creation of his poetry-presenting account. He discussed the potential outcomes of this move with many of his friends, most of their opinions encouraging with a slight resonance of disbelief and hesitation, many expressing their worries about taking any extreme risks in the direction of one's dreams. There were a lot of copyright issue excuses, worries about the public exposure and criticism as well as the feeling that the workload as it is, is enough for the boy and he should keep his mind on the job that pays for his rent and leave these more extravagant plans for the future. But the boy felt different. *The future is now* he reminded himself of the motto he saw on one of the magazines when he was younger, his opinion on the whole situation being rather wholesome. He was worried as one can be when their heart's work is exposed to the sight of these around him, he felt anxious about the creation of the site and knew that the workload he was handling at the time is enough to drive one to the grave prematurely. But his heartfelt something else as well. This insistent, constant echoing vibration within that did not let him fall asleep at night before making the wish for the next day to be full of creative magic, which so intensively engaged his mind whenever he would sit down to the page or the laptop, he knew he has to act upon. The need exceeded the want, desire overhauled the fear, he knew he is as ready as anyone could ever be, reminding himself of the dubious fact that *life does not wait for anybody.*

*

The site created, he sat down to his writings and chose a few to present as the first on the page, deciding which of them go well together, matching them by theme and date. There was plenty of poetry he wanted people to see, mostly due to its either uplifting or awareness rising quality. *The world is struggling as it is* he murmured, *I might as well try to make one person see it...* He felt the energizing emotion within his chest as the decision after decision, he filled the page with a few of his recent works. There was a little about the environment, some heart-breaking expression, and a discourse on the nature of creating art as he perceived it. Invigorated by this feeling of action he felt great.

The worry at the back of his mind, that which comes rising from the ego's little point of view, was still present but with each click of the button and upload seemed to lose its grip upon the boy's consciousness. He felt like he can achieve anything. Leaving the first few poems online, he turned off the app and laid down on his bed to relax for a moment and let the body and mind come to terms with this new state he was encountering. *Isn't it the same with Instagram or Facebook anyway* he pondered, *we constantly show ourselves to strangers through these platforms, just most of what we share is either phony or crap...* He smirked at his own perception and closed his eyes, taking a long breath. The recent turn of events brought him to exercise the power of the mind more often, meditation being the main motor for his practice and expansion of self-awareness. He liked those moments of calm, he genuinely enjoyed them. Letting the mind simmer as if left on the hob on low heat, he felt like his body truly rested all-the-while his awareness grew stronger and more self-validating for the reasons of resilience and relaxation. *It's a shift in the thinking that makes miracles happen* he quoted one of the books he read recently, letting the subconscious hear the thought manifest itself silently.

*

His belief in the Divine being a part of daily life grew stronger each day of his practice. *It's hard not to notice this outer dimension if you practice meditation often,* he thought, *it is quite a simple trick...* He didn't need to convince anyone of his belief, the belief being out of nature something a person either does or does not seem to be true. *What is true to one* he reminded himself, does *not have to be true to another... It's all a matter of perspective.* He liked the freedom that came with this way of thinking. *There is nothing to fight about if there is nothing, we do not consider better than another and as there are so many people on the planet it would be only silly to determine who is right,* he thought. A similar train of thought followed the idea of jumping off the building without the assurance that the net is present below. *Sometimes you just have to dive in,* he claimed, leaving the mind to do its magic as the thoughts flew by the window of his awareness like clouds traveling through the open sea of the sky
.

II.   Starting something completely new can feel overwhelming, but through diving in at the deep end, stepping outside our comfort zone, we grow with equally overwhelming speed...

The boy didn't know how to start at all. An idea, which was just a little seed of a concept, thrown into the soil of his mind, has taken him to take steps far from his known and comfortable environment. Suddenly, over few days, he was there, trying to screw on the microphone onto a tripod, which didn't seem to work properly *what the hell is wrong with this* he murmured, struggling with the newly purchased equipment. *Who you are to think you can podcast* the little devil on his shoulder hissed into the ear, *who would even listen anyway...?* The boy shrugged his shoulders, forcing the voice of his doubt to hold onto the collar of his jumper, distracting its attempts to discourage him. *It doesn't matter at the moment* he answered, feeling the excitement growing within him like a ball of a brightness sparkling in the middle of the night, *I'll worry about that when I record something...*

*

Finally, after a few deliberate attempts to understand the construction of the microphone and time spent organizing the necessary software on his laptop, the boy sat in front of the desk and looked beyond the thin layer of rounded filter, which hanged few inches away from the recording device *looks like an awfully dirty magnifying glass* he smirked. He planned to start recording in the night when the street outside his flat would become less noisy, people around letting it snooze a little before another busy day of service commence. He has spent the whole of the previous day infusing his brain with all kinds of tutorials and informational videos about the industry, activity, and subject of his endeavour. He watched professionals talking about the best choice of titles, logos creation, monetizing strategies, you name it. He noted down bullet points, but little of what he learned seemed to be of true value, most of the things being dependent on one particularly important, repeated in each video, aspect *'practice makes perfect'*. He knew it already. *Everybody knows it* he thought, *such a cliché...* Thinking of it though, he felt a familiar sense of unease and discomfort, which seemed to stem from somewhere between his ears. Aware of this feeling of the unknown, of stepping across the line, which he never considered to cross, his skin turned pale, his palms sweaty and cold. He was afraid. Afraid of all the possible mistakes, unfavourable comments, and displeased shakes of heads of those, who he wished to share this exciting adventure of his with. The little devil around his collar approached his ear again, spilling its poison straight through the membranes of his mind, *you won't manage...*

His hand travelled up towards his neck and tried to release the tension, which accumulated between his shoulders. The common sign of stress rang the bell of his mind police, organizing its troops to join his conquest and defeat the doubt, the biggest enemy of any great achievement in one's life. He took a deep breath in and closed his eyes, reminding himself that all that this experience of his is at the moment stems from the most common sabotage system known to man – fear. Revising the idea inside his mind, he exhaled trying to calm the pounding heart. *All that I see in the mind right now is just an illusion* he affirmed aloud, *mere conception conceived by my little self, that's all.* His voice, which felt hesitant didn't appeal to him, *how am I to speak with a voice like this...?* There were many reasons to disbelieve what the ego claimed, but the worry behind the sound of his voice was real and present, here, now. He thought of all the times, he heard himself speaking on camera, listening back to it, and crunching his face in displease for the tone and pitch of his voice. *Is this how I sound* he wondered. Having the worries inside his mind, the microphone ready to record on the desk, and the desire to make his dream come true, he picked up the phone and dialled the number of his father. Connection made; the signal of answering indicated by a sharp finish to the monotone buzz echoed across the ear of his. His father's voice followed *hello. Hi Dad,* he started, *I am struggling a little with my worries about the whole recording my voice thing and wanted to ask what you think of it...?* A moment of silence followed. His dad gathered his thoughts and cleared his throat before addressing the question. *Son* his deep voice addressed the boy, *as I understand it, the way we hear ourselves is far from how others do, and that is because whenever you talk, you hear it internally, through bones resonating rather than through your ears.* The boy nodded his head, trying to manipulate himself into thinking that this is sufficient encouragement to fight the doubt inside. *But there is another thing that I think you are asking about* his father continued, *and my answer to it is simple...* A moment of silence, which felt like an eternity to his young mind paused the world around him. *If you want to do something, if you feel the need to do it* his father's voice re-entered the space between them, no matter the distance, *if it is something that won't harm others and will fill your life with joy, just do it. Do not think about it, do not worry about the outcome, start right here, right now, and do what you can* he concluded, *and if you make mistake, so what... you will only get better through that. It's that simple.*

The boy thanked his father for the words of encouragement, which were probably truly what he called him for, even though the reasoning suggested otherwise. He put the phone down, looked at the microphone filter staring daringly into his face, and smiled slightly, feeling his hand trembling a little, *just wait till the night, you magnifying scarecrow.* The little hissing voice by his ear started back up again, but the boy didn't fancy listening to it anymore, standing up from his chair he snapped it off the shoulder and went out for a walk, it was time to think big dreams and worry about nothing.

It was time to act.

III.   *Everyone can start something; the true quest lies in finishing.*

The boy felt the shivers, the kind that only worry mixed with lack of conviction can bring. He was sitting at the desk in the morning hours of a working day and staring at his notebook he debated the sense of it all. His thoughts meandered down the stream of consciousness offering little help, as their variety and dualistic nature kept his mind busy trying to sieve the positive from the negative ones. It felt difficult. It was difficult. His recent efforts to create, promote and deliver led him to different emotional reactions, brought about his awareness by the unstoppable winds of change. *Is it good enough* his brain would argue, *is it true enough…?* Scratching his arm, he felt awkward with himself, recognizing that the opposition he was trying to overcome had its source within. *How to be stronger than yourself* he pondered, realizing the absurdity of the concept, and flipping the pages of the notebook looked for a quote that reminded him of this dilemma. His eyes scanned the scribbles, their form, and variety expressing the times of day and state of mind of his while noting them down. The search fuelled by the feel of need continued, as his mind rushed through the past writings allowing the palms to skip the pages as they felt. *Gotcha,* he heard within the mind, as the quote of a Greek philosopher was found. *The first and best victory is to conquer Self,* announced the words of Plato, *to be conquered by Self is of all things the most shameful and vile* suggested the second part.

*

The boy truly appreciated philosophy and for the past few years constantly searched for thoughts worth digesting, letting most of them become a part of his contemplations. Finding this one, he sat back on the chair and stared at the two-liner, considering his present struggle. He pondered on the signs, which could result in a conclusion that one was conquered by their Self, and trying to refer his efforts to the idea, he allowed his eyes to close for a moment.

Feeling more silent, as the outside world of light and colour became distant, he thought of the situations in his experience of life, that could have been considered defeats to the Self, reflecting on the past. It seemed easier to focus with the eyes closed, as there were fewer stimuli to give attention to. It appeared to him, that whatever we choose to do in life, a decision is involved. With that decision, each of us initiates a set of occurrences and actions, which in turn fuel the consecutive effects following the latter. It felt fascinating to consider what the 'free will' stands for, taking into consideration the circumstances that are brought upon us throughout our existence, but paying attention to the factor of the ego, the boy left this discourse for another day. Trying to reason with the nature of one's ego, he imagined a little animal, cornered, and petrified snarling towards anyone and anything that comes near. He chuckled upon such a vivid image painting itself within his head. *It's like the ego primarily wants to be safe* he reasoned, *who wouldn't though…? The only problem being, with constant safety there is no growth and without growth, there isn't much life either* he concluded.

*

Coming back to the initial thought and quote by Plato, the boy thought of the risks connected with being conquered by oneself. *It would probably mean allowing the fear and uncertainty to take charge of the actions* he pondered, *slowly but surely undermining the one true power of each of us… The belief in oneself* he murmured, letting the words spill around him, their echo ringing within his ears for another minute. Considering the facts and trying to unpack the worries that came with his recent projects, he thought of the usefulness, which came from allowing the doubt to simmer in his heart. *Can save my life when crossing the street* he considered, *but surely there is little if any positive payoff from anticipating a failure of my creative work…* Remembering the idea of Inner Critic from The Artist's Way[4] book, as well as bringing up the self-mastery advocated so strongly by Thich Nhat Khan in his work The Art of Living[5] he decided to let his ego crawl back to its cave and let him enjoy the creation he was undertaking. *The difference between starting something and bringing it to finish is major* he thought, *one is only faced with the opposition of initial worry and doubt, the second with these two and the whole army of others, who came to support the failures of that initial pair…*

---

[4] J. Cameron. *The Artist's Way: A Spiritual Path to Higher Creativity*, Main Edition, London: Souvenir Press, 2020
[5] Thich Nhat Hanh. *The Art of Living: Peace and Freedom in the Here and Now*, New York: Harper Collins USA, 2017

Applying the same technique used in writing, when the adversity from within seems to block the flow, which can only be overrun by persistent creation, the boy waved his hand letting the smoke of self-doubt dissolve into the air around him and mix with the subtle scent of the incense stick burning slowly by the window. *Start what is worth finishing and finish what is worth starting* he wrote on the page, a little smile lingering on his face.

ABOUT BEING

I.   *Did you hear about the fifty-two hertz whale* asked a friend one
        day, as they strolled down the coastal path, looking out to the
        ocean.

The boy shook his head and squinted his eyes, whose wellbeing was being
threatened by the late afternoon sun. His friend waited a moment before
continuing, as if building the suspense, before presenting this, what the boy
assumed to be, quite a strange phenomenon. *So,* he started, waving his hand
towards the water, and taking a long breath in, *the scientists have recently
discovered a whale, whose frequency is so different than all the other
whales, that it is impossible for it to communicate with anyone else.* The
boy savoured the new information, like one does with a sip of a good, old
whisky, and glancing at his companion, smiled wow… *I bet it must be quite
a lonely fellow.* They laughed briefly, even though both felt for the
mentioned creature. *Imagine how hard it must be* he continued *like, if you
or I were not able to learn any language at all, even if we were really
trying…* His friend nodded his head. *That's mental* he concluded. They
continued the walk without talking, each considering the fate of the unlucky
giant, whose life must have been one of the loneliest one there is. The boys'
mind raced, as he tried to comprehend how this kind of situation could take
place in nature. *Isn't nature supposed to be perfectly balanced* he thought,
*does that mean there is a whale somewhere out there that can communicate
with all kinds of frequencies…?* He shared the questionable theory with his
friend, and they discussed all the possibilities, including the idea of multiple
universes, whales being only an illusion, and the prospect of finding a lost
civilization, whose pillar of existence depends on the level of frequency of
all the swimming giants around. The conversation meandered through
down the topic, like a river making its way through forestry area of the
globe, pushing through, squeezing between, and overcoming the most
immaculate obstacles that a nature can create. They laughed quite a bit,
arriving occasionally to a conclusion so ridiculous, that even a fifty-two
hertz whale seemed like a mundane 'fun fact' in the prospect of seeing these
'ideas' coming to life. Their talk had no particular order, letting the minds
wander, they created new scenarios, possible solutions, and challenges, that
seemed to be more or less possible in this world, which considering the
existence of such a whale, might as well allow any other 'anomalies' to
have their place. The boy thought of the hardship of that creature, imagining
himself being unable to speak in any language ever; not even sign language
or a Morse Code.

The prospect of such tragedy drew blood towards his spine and made his back twitch with cortisol levels rising. The mind automatically opposed the possibility of such a misery. The boy noticed the reaction of the body and tried to loosen up by making out another joke on the whales' account. *I know* he thought *that's not too nice but come on… the whale wouldn't be able to understand and get upset anyway…* Letting themselves have a few more laughs, they arrived at the pier and made their way towards the water, sitting down on the side of the wooden 'bridge' that connected the ocean with the beach. Struggling with the sun, which appeared to be punishing their eyes for the laughs on whales' account, they sat facing away from it and looked towards the seafront, where many people strolled down the path, having their own little world of conversations. The boy imagined the life of the whale, who unable to connect with anyone else, roams the words vastest oceans in search for understanding and acceptance. Weirdly enough, he felt a strong empathy to its troubles, reminiscing on all the times, where he himself, misunderstood by others, had to deal with what was, as it unfolded, without anyone's help or understanding. *Isn't each of us sometimes like that whale* he said out loud, not planning to and drew attention of his friend to that point of view. His friend looked at him surprised and was about to laugh, but he stopped himself. They sat there in silence for a moment, trying to reason with the point made by their minds. After a while, his friend nodded his head slightly, as if he didn't particularly want to, but had no other choice. *I guess you are quite right* he said. Savouring the concept, they sat there swimming in the mental ocean of thoughts, conclusions, and possible alternatives, none of which provided a getaway from the idea that each of us has at some point felt like that misunderstood whale. The boy thought of the multitude of people that roam this Earth, everyday dying, coming to life, marrying each other, achieving goals, losing it all, trying too hard, making mistakes, organising something new, following a well-worn path, and all the other inbetweeners, realising that not one of them could go through their existence without being misunderstood at some point in their life. He thought of the differences in experience, age, thought processes, upbringing, opportunities, luck, attitudes, ideas, wishes, tastes, drives and emotional states, as well as the looks of everyone of this planet. He thought of all that, only to come back to the first assumption, again and again reinforcing the idea that everyone has more in common with the fifty-two hertz whale, that they have with any other of the swimming giants out there. Surprised with his conclusions he looked at the friend, whose concerned face seemed to paint a similar picture of acknowledgment of the subject.

Their laughs long gone, they appeared sadder than ever before, realising how much ignorance they have presented, when initially laughing at the fate of this unlucky creature. Speechless, they sat there looking out to the ocean. The boy thought of the idea that there is a part of every creature in everyone; about the possibility that each existence is a sum of all others added and subtracted in a natural, organised in its randomness, order. He thought of his life, which, unfolding without a stop, offered glimpses to existences of other species, people, entities and things. He thought of how sometimes, a person might feel like a cheeky fox, when in attempts to beat the system, they cheat on the exam; or how they might sometimes act like an ostrich, whose panicky reaction leads them to hide away from lives' problems instead of 'facing the music'. He thought of all the times he felt like a little insect, whose life so fragile, hangs on the thread of reality, whenever upon crossing the street in a busy city, he almost lost his right to exist. Imagining all these scenarios, reminding himself of all the mistakes, shortcomings, achievements, miracles, and situations of all kinds, that manifested in his journey along the years, he realised that none of us actually gets away with life without facing the problems, that everyone else has faced in one way or another. To his surprise, he felt relieved coming to this kind of conclusion. It felt, as if some weight has been lifted of the shoulders, as he listed all the examples, that proved the argument to be quite true, even if only to certain extent. He sighed out his worries, feeling a little closer with the fifty-two hertz whale and its struggle. His friend noticed the transformation and without saying a word, he seemed to relax a little more as well. They continued their quiet contemplation, staring into the distance, letting their minds wander the realms of ideas, concepts, and conclusions, from which none offered a fully comprehensive outcome. Thinking about the lonely whale, the boy looked towards the people walking on the shore, living their lives in their own little bubbles of understanding and misconceptions, each of them following a different thought, that echoed through the voids of their consciousness as they continued their endeavour in this realm of ours. *Maybe* he thought *there is a bit of that whale in each of us… maybe all we do throughout our lives is trying to be understood by others… maybe sometimes we achieve that understanding and sometimes we don't.* The boy smiled to his thoughts as the last one - a conclusive one emerged, *maybe all this existence is, is a little rehearsal of what could and couldn't be and we are all just trying to grasp it as we go…*

II. Words, as the expression of thoughts, have the power to transcend the present state regardless of space and time we find ourselves in…

The rain tapped against the stretched hat of the umbrella. The rhythmical symphony of nature's very best life-sustaining liquid caressed the cover of the boy's body. He was walking down the road at a steady pace, his face covered by the shadow of the item held above his head. His shoes and pants-covered legs were the only visible parts of his demeanour when observed from the eagle's perspective. He must have looked like a steady-sliding rounded creature pacing across the town's pavements. It was late, with midnight creeping up quietly, as he continued his prolonged conversation over the phone. It was becoming a routine to chat late at night during these quiet-street walks, and the boy appreciated these moments of calm more and more. He wondered if this appreciation means he was getting old…

*

Their discussion meandered across the planes of thought-processes, political issues, nature of reality, and everything in-between. Neither an obvious beginning, nor a specific ending was to be found in their discourse, and more often than not the main theme of the conversation did not adhere to any straightforward interpretation of itself. They were just talking. Just talking.

*

Kicking the little stone, which the boy approached and noticed a few seconds before sending it flying through space, he listened to her story. There wasn't anything special in the way he listened, neither was there any magical characteristics in the way she spoke. Yet they appeared to enjoy the experience thoroughly. The boy pondered on the subject, thinking of just how much of one's existence comes down to the perception of it. He recognized again and again just how much time one could spend talking, without realizing the passage of time. It worked both ways, as there could have been a difficult experience to talk through which momentary nature could stretch out into the seemingly never-ending discourse, as well as there were times when a mere pleasantry of conversation would bring one to the realization that the past few hours just flew by without notice. He remembered the statement made by one of the prominent figures, whose influence shaped the minds of many people at the time, and still does influence some and recited it in his brain quietly – *It's all in the mind.*

His pace didn't rush but wasn't too slow either. There was a certain reassurance in the act of walking during phone calls, which the boy couldn't yet fully describe or analyse. *Maybe it's just me who needs to move when I talk,* he reasoned, *if it is so, does it make me feel good or bad though...?* He listened to the echo of the words spoken in a conceptual past by the girl, whose voice shimmered on the other end of their call and thinking of what she was trying to express he thought of his point of view. Their talks were far from ideal, sometimes slightly profound, sometimes rather dull, but always somehow flawless in their seamless flow of spontaneity. *They remind me of the thought process during writing* he considered, *surprising oneself with each word one makes...*

*

He switched hands, putting the umbrella onto the left side of his face, and placing his cheek against the cold, wooden handle closed his eyes. Listening to the voice, which at that moment expressed its opinion about the sound created by a ticking clock, the boy left his own body and for a moment of subtle absence allowed his awareness to rest on the bed next to the person speaking. It was possible, because the ultimate inside feeling of one is free from space or time, given the environment to shift one's focus. His imagination felt the soft surface of the bedding and sent a suggestive sensation across the boy's cheek's nervous web. His legs moved mechanically, his ears listened to both the rain's concert and the girl's voice, but his mind was elsewhere. For that split second in infinity; a moment so trivial in the larger scheme of things; a grain in the sand resting at the bottom of Universe's ocean, his perspective has shifted. It was as everything in one's life truly is usual, casual, unimportant, simple. *But it was, and usually when something is, it is better than most ever would.*

ABOUT SYNCHRONICITY

I.   *Some call it coincidence, some say it's a part of the 'chaos' of the universe, but I believe it's much more than that…*

The boy was sat on the beach, leaning on his backpack, which overflowing with cold beers and snacks kept its form only thanks to the few strong side stitches. The boy was not much of a boy anymore considering his age, but his feelings of the world and curiosity of what's around him still resembled that of an adolescent. He sipped a cold beer pondering the sentence that manifested within his mind, as he watched the sea waves come and go in the never-ending dance of change. He was away on holidays with friends and grasped each moment with his whole self, trying to create as many good memories as possible, given a restricted time and opportunity to do so. One of his mates was in the sea, crashing his bare chest against the cold water, while the others sat on the shore scattered among the backpacks, bags of food, and towels covered in sand. The boy was a thinker, or at least he considered himself to be such. It wasn't far from the truth because as his mother stated in one of their recent discussions, he was 'always much calmer than other kids', playing with Lego blocks and cars instead of running around the room, shouting. In contrast to one of his early age friends, he was considered even slightly 'too calm'. His mother often used the term 'little buddha', as in his early years he was a bit too fat for a child, constantly eating and sitting rather than moving around most of the time. The boy felt that this was true to his nature even now, much later in life, with all the experiences and shortcomings of a young human that he was. Having recently discovered the term 'synchronicity' and explored many ideas emanating from Buddhism and other philosophies, the boy was becoming a man, thinking of what the 'true nature of existence' and his own 'truth' is. *To tell the truth,* he thought, *one would have to abandon all that is human since human nature is that which restricts us (humans) to see the bigger picture.* His consideration to nature didn't come and go as he pleased, it just sorts of manifested itself every now and then, instantly making a shift in his perception of reality and motivating him to look within for answers, which as one could guess, didn't come easily. In this constant search for meaning, the boy explored ideas and concepts of many greats before his time and often arrived at the similar conclusion, that there are things in life, events, phenomena, and situations that nothing but the existence of a Higher Power of some sort, can explain. Trying to piece the 'truth' together, he encountered the idea of 'synchronicity', which became a big part of his daily thoughts and considerations.

Trying to see, what is all the fuss about, he noticed more and more situations that suggested the idea to be real and true to the flow of life. *Everything happens as it should, with us only realizing it as we pay attention to the detail and keep an open mind,* he recited the knowledge gained from the books, as he gazed into the sea. *Synchronicity is noticing those situations, events, and things that occur in order and with a purpose according to the law of interdependence,* he reminded himself.

*

The waves came and went, their white fringes tall and splashing, leaving marks of moisture on the sand in front of his feet. His friend sat by his side pointed into the distance, somewhere a few meters away from their place of rest – *look, that's a kid's shovel,* he exclaimed. The boy looked towards the item and noticed the green handle twirling between the waves, about to hit the shore. Without a moment of hesitation, letting his life energy and intuition take charge, he jumped to his feet and ran towards the toy, catching it just before the wave was able to swallow it back into the sea. He waved it above his head in the sign of triumph and approached the rest of his group, leaving the shovel on the side to dry. *I'm going to give it to some lucky kid,* he decided to think of this as an opportunity to make someone smile today. Grateful for this chance, he laid down on the sand, leaning on his backpack, and grabbed another beer. *Time to relax and enjoy the views again,* he thought looking to the horizon, letting his mind wander.

*

Time passed. Waves came and went. The wind turned a few times, leaving the windbreakers of those few lucky owners useless until set differently. The sun shuffled in its place, leaning more and more towards the sea. The boy and his friends drank and talked, laughed, and played card games, ate their snacks, and took photos of the beautiful views. All was good and in its rightful place. After some time one of his friends picked up the shovel and started digging, claiming that this item belongs to him now and it is truly lucky that the boy had found one. The boy smiled, leaving the words at the back of his throat, pondering on who should be given the toy after all. *I think I'll give it to some kid on the way back* he said, surprising others with his wish, but none claimed otherwise. Exactly then, at that moment in time when the boy was expressing his plan, a father and a son approached the group, leaving everyone suddenly quiet and reserved. *Excuse me, lads,* the man said, *my son has lost this shovel into the sea today earlier on and I was wondering if it's possible to get it back.* The man pointed at the toy, which rested in the hands of the boys' friend.

Everyone was so surprised, no one has said a word. The boy got up looking at the two arrivals and smiled opening his palms to the sky. *I found it in the sea a few moments ago sir,* the boy said, *it will be a pleasure to give it to your son, with whom it belongs.* His friend reached out, leaving the toy with the boy, whose face brightened with a smile. His father grateful for their action thanked the boy and his friends and the two left promptly. All the boys' friends were speechless, including the boy, who sat down on the sand and closed his eyes with a smile ripping through his cheeks. *Everything is how it should be,* he reminded himself. He looked towards the sea. *Thank you for this moment of synchronicity and the chance to experience it,* he said. He turned to his best friend, who was sat by his side, and smiled wider, reaching the peak of his smiling abilities, *that is what synchronicity is all about... beautiful.* They sat there on the beach, breathing in the salted air, drinking yet another cold beer, thinking of all those moments of pleasure in life, from which those that have additional meaning of the value of gratitude and politeness to one another seemed the most worth living for.

II.   *They were sat on the beach, wine and cigarettes leading the way of the party. The wind howled down the sandy planes, gaining on strength with each moment. The storm was coming.*

One of the boy's friends checked the weather forecast online. It wasn't looking hopeful. They considered going back to the camp, looking towards the horizon, which darkening gradually offered not much of a comfort. *If we go back now, we have a chance to prepare for it* someone claimed, trying to convince the group of the next move. *I don't mind a little rain* someone else concurred. It took some time, but the decision was made and with slightly lower enthusiasm, they made their way back through the forest. *Let's come up with some plan* the gears of the mind turned, *there is too many of us to fit under that tent roof though...*

*

The party continued at the campsite. They stood around drinking and smoking, the wind gaining on strength but being ignored more as they were close to their tents and cars. The boy was in quite a state. He looked around, sipping the wine straight from the bottle, *what could work as a rain cover for us...?* His friend struggled to stick a little waterproof blanket onto the ropes, which held the roof of their tent. They needed something bigger. The boy walked across their camp and remembering a pile of trash, which someone must have left before they arrived, he picked up a big, dark blue, piece of something that resembled a waterproof cover from an industrial site.

Springing the water drops all around, he pulled it out of the bushes and still unaware of how lucky the finding was, asked one of his friends to give him a hand. *That's synchronicity* the boy thought. His friend couldn't believe his eyes. Once spread on the floor, the material seemed huge, wide enough to keep all of them safe from the rain. The boy rushed around, finding pieces of rope to tie it with, and encountered a large chunk of it, folded underneath that same pile of trash. *That's amazing* his friend announced, realizing the luck in which they found themselves, *you're the hero of tonight bro!* The boy thought differently. Believing in synchronicity, which seemed pervasive in his life over the past months, he was certain of the way it worked its magic.

*

The wind gained on strength, offering a little incentive to make the effort of preparing the campsite before the storm hits. With the help of two others, they managed to fix the material across the treetops and tied it down in four places. It quickly turned out that one of the boy's friends brought a rope with him. *Obviously* - the boy thought. The group celebrated the fact that the party won't stop, gathering underneath the provisional roofing. They were ready for the storm, or at least that's what they thought.

*

Once the storm arrived, the roof exposed its faulty construction. It was too light from the side, which was hit by the wind the most, which caused it to fly up and offer no cover from the heavy rain at all. They had to take it down a little. Struggling against the rain, which struck their faces without a stop, they pulled the cover down more and more, until all were essentially sat underneath a pile of tarpaulin. The water flowed down the corners of their cover and every now and then they had to empty it by pushing the middle of the 'tent' up and out. This was far from comfortable and a few of them constantly did so. The boy sat next to his friend for some time, trying to come up with something to change their situation. They agreed to act as soon as the rain weakens. It took some time but as it did, they left the group and instinctively approached that same pile of trash, which offered such a great piece of help before. The boy picked up a broken piece of a metal pole and his friend found an empty crate of beer. Yet again they have saved the day. Setting the crate in the middle of their gathering and fixing the pole inside, they ended up with just what they needed. The group was in awe. It was heart-warming for the boy to hear his friends expressing their happiness, which his findings brought.

He smiled and thanked humbly, understanding that it was nothing that his own self could have achieved without the pervasive power of synchronicity, which prevailed in his life more often these days.

Believing that it 'was supposed to happen this way' he thanked whatever the power was behind it and laughed at the situation, which turned out just the way they needed it to. *Even if it is just pure luck, I like the idea that it is something more…*

III.   *It's a matter of a chance whether something takes place or not, but in our intention lies a power to make this chance higher than ever…*

The boy was already for five days in the middle of what seemed like a flowing, living river of situations and opportunities. He noticed so many situations that screamed of the chance that whatever happens, comes along in a natural, smooth manner, that his excitement and satisfaction of this 'flow' became the focus of his acceptance. Pieces of the trash put together with a little tape changed their essence and utilized in a witty manner, became like new things in themselves. The boy has noticed these little parts of chances, which when used wisely transformed offering the necessary thing. In the need of the rain, they found a tarpaulin, ropes, and a pole to keep it up. *Maybe it would be best to say those things found them, rather than another way around, but who is the one to state these things* the boy thought. They were looking for a bottle of cheap wine and on the onset of belief and a little action, the boy managed to deliver the lost item, regardless of the 'hopelessness' of the situation in the eyes of the wine owner. Those little moments made him believe and notice this idea of synchronicity a little more.

*

They partied yet another day at the campsite, which at this point was more like a swampy encampment or a little village. The overall spirit of the party was great, and their drinking continued until the late hours of the night. Going to the beach to continue intoxication they found themselves talking about things much greater in size and comprehension than themselves. They looked up the sky considering the chances of there being something more or less similar to the contemporary idea of God sold to them by the church, in which their country seemed to be included. Discussing the chances of it all they drank away, letting the mind swallow all that it could and give the expected smoothening of the situation in exchange. Time passed letting the smoke shimmer and disappear on the wind around them.

Finally, after hours of fun, they decided to take it back to the tent city, in which their swamp resided. Their smiles invisible in the darkness of the night gleamed with an energetic load of pure happiness, which comes into life in any situation of connectedness between people.

*

They walked back to the camp, while one of the boys started doubting the situation, he found himself in. The keys to his car were gone and his fear of loss grew. He walked back with them, announcing the situation as they were about to continue drinking under their tarpaulin. *I don't have my keys* he exclaimed, fearing the worst, *I need them tomorrow for fucks sake...!* A few of them looked at him, most ignoring the situation as alcohol buzzed in their minds stronger than the words of his. The boy decided to help. He knew from experience how it is to lose something important to the vastness of the beach in this exact place, a few years back, and wanted to help to avoid this situation for his friend. *We'll find them don't worry* he said, feeling the doubt of a lie within. *Is it a lie though* he pondered, as they looked through the bag of his mate. *I bet I left them on the beach* his friend pleaded, agitated of the arising situation. There was no other way to find them than to go and have a look, and so they did. Leaving the group behind, they walked back through the forest, taking a look with a dim flashlight at each piece of trash on the path in the woods. The search has begun.

*

Taking little steps and consecutive turns after enough steps, they looked through the part of the beach that seemed the most accurate to their place of stay a little earlier that night. The boy was still hopeful, but each moment seemed to draw more and more on the energy connected with doubt. Their chances were faint, and they knew it, even though their mouths kept shut as they roamed through the sand. Empty bottles left on the side indicated their presence around the area and with hopes slightly higher, they looked through each part of the sand without a break. The boy was tired and drunk but the need for finding the keys was stronger than any of this. His friend knew the same, his eyes slightly sunk, his smile dimmed with fear, he continued the search. It is hopeless the boy thought. *We will find it bro* the boy affirmed, patting his colleague's arm. With a nod of the head, they agreed it is probably time to go back. Even if they are here his friend underlined, we probably patted it down even more... They walked back in silence.

129

The campsite was as always, heaving with the party, which never seemed to end. They walked into their little area and rested among the others. The boy felt defeated, his belief of synchronicity losing its grip as there seemed to be no hope of finding his friend's precious keys. The owner of the lost item sat in the chair, writing up a message for his friend to explain why his ability to drive back to meet with her tomorrow fainted away. Their spirit weakened. The boy felt sick of it, unable to accept what has taken place. *History likes to repeat itself* he thought remembering his loss of a phone a few years back, *what a life...* They sat in the darkness, the dim light underneath the tarpaulin providing less and less reassurance. *This is what happens when hope leaves the room* the boy thought. As his friend picked up his backpack to have the last, rather angry look through the pockets, annoyed at the situation, his face changed. He pulled out a piece of something metallic from within and jingled it with a smile beaming from his eyes, which glistened in the darkness. *I found them, bro* he exclaimed lacking the belief in what has taken place, *I actually found them!*

*

The boy and his friend were sat on the chairs underneath their little rain cover. They patted their backs unable to hold back the satisfaction. *I knew we would find it* his friend affirmed, amazed at the luck that yet again manifested in their little getaway. *I accepted the defeat* already the boy answered, smiling with a positive surprise. *What a luck* - they exhaled. *We wanted it bad enough for it to happen, that's all...*

> II.   *Sometimes in life things just happen the way we feel they should to such an extent that we consider these phenomena to be 'miracles'... Through constant recognition of them though, we can attract more and more to the point when the day seems to just flow perfectly. Yesterday was just such a day, full of synchronicity, wonders, and joy of recognizing them all.*

The boy was sat at his desk looking outside the window, which still covered in the morning frost was only partly transparent. The hour was early, therefore barely anyone could be spotted on the street. He looked at his laptop, as the home screen loaded and opened the new file, creating yet another of many writing projects, he's been working on for the past months. *Day of miracles* he typed the title on the top of the page and yawning joyfully started writing. He wanted to reflect upon the day before, which seemed to him so absurdly perfect in its flow and occurrences that he decided to record it through the medium of creative writing *it was just too good to let it slip without noting* he thought.

The mentioned day started for him even earlier than today. He got out of bed and seeing the sun rising on the horizon, painting the sky with orange and pink colours, he quickly dressed up and ran outside to have a morning run, as he planned the day before. The run in the morning sun invigorated him and raised his morale substantially.

*

It was his day at the office, which meant climbing the hill up to the university as well as hours spent on his own in the space, where there is nothing more than his work laptop and Starbucks coffee shop across the hall. He didn't mind working there, but considering the comfort of his workspace back home, he preferred the days, when all he needed to do to go to work, was to dress up the top of his clothing. Sometimes he wouldn't even bother wearing pants, as the video calls were always with the camera showing you from the belly up. Of course, he couldn't get up during those calls, but being aware of the risk, he didn't worry too much *you can always turn off the camera as well* he would remind himself.

*

After the run, he did a bit of yoga and stretched on the floor to meditate, which always felt great after exercising. Once the mind settled and his breathing slowed down, he continued with his morning routine, brushing his teeth, taking a shower, and sitting down to write down a few pages of journaling and creative ideas, that came to his awareness throughout the exercises. With the head empty of worries and full of positive energy, he felt like a charged battery ready to brighten up the day. He ate a small breakfast, prepared something for lunch at the office, and taking a cup of coffee-to-go, he left the flat, heading towards the University. Music blasted through his headphones, as he crossed the street and waved to one of his friends who met him on the way. His pace steady and fairly fast, as usual, pushed his person upwards, fighting against the gravity and incline of the hill *I will never miss* this he smirked. Back where he came from, his town and most of his homeland, to be honest, was rather flat, with only three lanes of mountains being present in the southern part of the country. Over the years of studying and working here, he got used to the hilly side of things, but he looked forward to abandoning the place in the search for somewhere slightly flatter and less inclined, especially if such a walk was to be done every single day. He was almost halfway up the hill when a car horn's noise reached his ears underneath the headphones. He looked towards the street confused and smiled cheerfully, spotting one of his workmates in the car, waving his hand at him *come on*, his lips seemed to exclaim.

The boy looked down the street, let a car go past, and ran across to join the vehicle of his friend *what a luck* - he thought *pure synchronicity…*

*

Once at work, his laptop unpacked and set up on the desk, which was his, for the time being, he sat down and looked at his little notecard with all the things 'to do' on the day, scribbled with a black ink pen.

*

The plan of the day wasn't too busy, filled mostly with meetings, emails to send, and a few film editing jobs that he was going to finish once back home, as he left his laptop to work on videos behind. The day at work has started and slamming out task after task, the boy was crossing out each target planned for today. At some point during one of the meetings, the boy's coffee was finished. He looked at the empty cup and thought of the wish to buy himself a Mocha from the café across the hall. His mind wrestled with reason, as he realized both its prize being a little excessive, as well as understanding that all he is feeling is a sensation of craving. He didn't need the coffee, he just wanted it. *It's fine you had one already* he commandeered his body and clasping his palms together, tried to catch up with the meeting conversation, which continued on-screen.

*

Video-call was planned to last at least an hour, and so by the time knocking on the door to his office filled the room, the boy forgot about the need for coffee. He managed to let it go. *Yes,* he muted his microphone and shouted towards the door, *can I help you?* A lady from the café entered, carrying a cup of coffee, and looked at him smiling. *Hello sweetheart, would you by any chance want to take this Mocha from me* she started, *some student has ordered it and then decided it's not what he wanted so… I don't want to pour it away you see…* The boy's mind was blown. He stared at the large cup of coffee, which he was going to buy but decided not to, and smiled in confusion and excitement, *of course, that would be amazing* he answered, *thank you so much, you're an angel!* The lady chuckled and left the cup of a hot drink on the side of his desk, *have a nice day sweetheart* she added, leaving the room. *Have a great day* he shouted behind her, *that's amazing!* His face beaming with joy, he unmuted his microphone and raised the cup in front of the camera, *I just got given a free Mocha!* He sipped his gift slowly, enjoying each sip of the warming, sweetly chocolatey drink and thought of the absurdity of the number of 'synchronic' events that took place today, *and the day has only started* the thought echoed through his mind.

The more you look for the clues of the universal laws, the more you find them in your daily life…

The boy arrived at the airport a few hours before his flight. Leaving the train station, he walked across the vast airport, which due to the recent events and world-encompassing pandemic was almost empty. All of the shops closed, restaurants abandoned, only one café still open, serving takeaway drinks and food on the go. He stopped by the stand with cold snacks and refreshments and searching for the item, which would tickle his fancy, he overheard a dialogue. Taking off his headphones, he looked at the two women waving their hands erratically. One of them spoke English, trying to get a certain answer of the other, which quite obviously did not speak this language at all. The boy took a step forward listening to the mumbled words coming out of the older lady's mouth, which covered by the mask did not sound to hearable. He heard a keyword, which suggested to him that the customer might be a Russian speaker. Gathering his courage, he stepped in asking if he could help. The café worker looked at him and explained briefly that the lady is talking a foreign language. The boy turned to the older woman and asked *paruski,* looking for a sign of acknowledgment. Her eyes brightened up as she heard a familiar word. She nodded energetically and pointed at the apple juice bottle, which the worker held in her hand. *Ckolko stoit* she murmured, alongside a line of words, which the boy didn't manage to understand. *How much is it* he turned to the worker, *let me see* she answered with visible relief. She walked away towards the till, as the boy stood next to the old woman trying to understand her words, which seemed to continue without a stop. *I can barely understand* he thought feeling a wave of stress arise, as he blushed. *Good that we wear masks at least* his mind added, *at least she won't see my reaction…* Listening to his thoughts he instantly slapped them in the face, *what are you even worried about… be proud you can help her in Russian, which you started to self-learn not that long ago!* His slight nod comforted the lady, as she stopped talking and looked at the clerk, who came back with the bottle *it's two pounds.* The boy smiled, quickly realizing the mask is stopping the smile from its appearance, and looked at the Russian speaker *dwa funta*, he said mimicking the app's lesson. She understood. He sighed with relief and ordered his coffee.

ABOUT POTENTIALITY

I.   *There isn't a thing created by a human, that wouldn't be initiated with an idea. This lies at the root of everything and anything our species will ever achieve…*

The boy was running up the hill, breathing heavily, as his chest puffed up and squeezed in with each round of air grasping struggle. It was early in the morning on a Sunday and as it usually happens, he was all by himself outside at this time. The town was still asleep, its colourful houses hiding the citizens underneath their variously formed roofs. He reached the smaller peak of the hill and choosing the space facing the ocean sat down, crossing his legs, and straightening his back. It just so happened that he decided not to take his headphones and the phone on the run, so sitting there at the edge of the cliff, he listened to the waves rhythmically splashing against the rocks beneath. He closed his eyes and reminding himself of the quote he heard the day before, which inspired him to recollect if there was anything in his life, he didn't do, have or become following an initial idea of some kind. His mind wandered the vast plains of memory fields, as he reminisced about his choices all the way back until he could remember, which must have been somewhere around his early childhood years. He thought of the choice of the job applications, women he dated, the items that became his possessions and took their place in his room in one year or another, his friendships, schools were chosen and graduated from, his hobbies, his achievements, and failures, the sets of Lego blocks wished for during his early years birthdays and Christmas Eve's, he considered them all and surprising himself came to the conclusion that truthfully there was not one thing among these, that wouldn't be initiated by an idea. True, some of these ideas were inspired by other people, some by his 'hunches', some even by an impulse of desire on the spot there and then, but none of them was free of the associated initial thought of willingness to pursue it. Shocked with his conclusion, he opened the eyes and winced mechanically, as if his body didn't fully acknowledge the confusing results of his contemplation.

*

The boy continued his run almost unaware of the whole running happening, as his mind wandered off concerned with the whole fact he has discovered, once more leaving the body in a state of habitual activity. He would probably fall over already if it wasn't that the months of morning runs have become a routine of his as well. His shoes pounced up and down across the seafront path, as he pondered on the second part of the whole idea that was presented with that quote he thought of earlier.

As he recollected the speaker has offered a thesis that whatever one holds in his mind, whatever one can imagine; conjure in their creative awareness, one can bring into the physical realm, therefore making it his own... The boy considered it to be quite an empowering thought, but that's only what he considered it at the time, a thought. Now after coming to understand the genuine meaning and accuracy of the first part, he dared to consider the second half to be true as well, and if it was...

*

He ran thinking of the dreams and plans he used to recognize as too big and too absurd to ever become true, now seeing them all in a different light. *If that statement is true* his mind murmured, again and again, *then anything I can dream of I can achieve... Anything...* He squinted his eyes in the morning sun, which just appeared on the horizon, announcing the beginning of the day, and struggling to come to terms with this new point of view, he ran up the castle ruins, meandering between the gravel-covered in plants and grass, its emergence dating back more than hundreds of his lifetimes. He liked the place, as it felt humbling to be present in the space, which once was the main part of the town, now degraded into the few shapeless walls. *It's all a matter of time* he pondered standing at the edge of the hill, on which the castle was set. His mind was working on a hyper-speed, rendering all of his considerations as well as providing stable input for the body to continue these sporadic changes in speed and direction, as the run was still very much so in progress. His heart was pounding, trying to free itself from the sweat-covered chest. The boy stretched his arms wide, letting the wind embrace his warmed up, slightly stiff from the night's sleep, body. The tear of sweat trickled down his eyebrow and landed on his jumper, by his collarbone. He felt alive and intensively aware, as his consciousness began to accept and adjust its priorities for days to come, with the knowledge from the quote taken into consideration. He felt like there was a direction and a goal to achieve and as much as he was sometimes lazy, there was not a better motivation for him to do anything in the world than the possibility of success. At least that's what the personality test at his work has announced a few months before. The boy smirked, remembering the results of that multiple answers examination, thinking of it as a rather overrated way of bracketing people. *Fair play to them though, whoever came up with it* he murmured, *I ain't no psychologist after all, so it's not for me to judge.* Nevertheless, he didn't like the idea of putting people into any boxes or categories at all, as he considered everyone to be so different and unique it was rather impossible to have them all catalogued.

It was his opinion and so he didn't take the test to heart that much but realizing how intensively the sudden revelation and motivation for growth has shaken him, he had to admit that the makers of it were right about something... He smiled and nodded his head slightly, letting the sign of regard for those 'specialists' echo throughout the universe, *fair play.*

*

Once he reached his flat, he took a quick shower and sat down to eat breakfast, at the same time looking through the internet in the search for the author of the quote. He found out the title of the book, which treated the subject, and once writing its title down, he decided to order it from the online shop to be delivered as soon as possible. Only a few months later was he to discover that it was this book that has made people like Bill Gates, Oprah, Warren Buffett, and many more the successful people they are today. The boy has discovered a book, that in a matter of time was to become his most important daily read and forever change the way he was to go about his life. He had no idea at the time, just how important this thought quoted and contemplated upon would become to him.

II. *The greatest limit of one's potential is their own belief in themselves...*

The boy was standing in the lake, his neck, and shoulders still visible above the surface. It was cold. So cold, there was a mist of steam hanging above the water, as the temperature difference between the lake and the air was so great. *Must be below zero* he pondered gazing in the distance. Breathing deeply and slowly, he felt fixed in place, like a tree in the forest's floor grounded with its roots. His friend standing next to him was similarly still and far away with his thoughts, as they waited for the healing time to pass. The watch signalled the six-minute goal reached, and the boy hesitated, thinking of emerging from the freezing bath already. His mate turned his head and smiled; *can we add another four...? I guess we can* the answer rang in the boy's throat, as he clicked the watch's button trying to stay as motionless as possible, *it hurts less if you stay still...*

*

It was amazing how far they have gone already. Having participated only three times in these morning cold sessions, the boy went from lasting three minutes up to ten. All within a week time of training. *Crazy* the boy thought, *no one could have convinced me to such possibility for myself before trying* he concluded.

136

Using the time of heightened focus and quiet awaiting, he considered the potentiality, which lingers in each individual, yet so seldom is it recognized and acted upon. *Why is that* he asked himself, shifting his weight slightly forward, as his toes went numb and he anticipated falling into the water, *why do we have so much disbelief in our abilities...?* Recounting the experiences of the past, he felt inspired, as there were a few recognizable traits that divided failure from success in any area of life. It was obvious to him that persistence and self-discipline played a major part in most of his endeavours but struck by this feeling of confidence about his ability to stand in the freezing water for so long made him wonder about the most important factor – belief. *Rarely does someone manage to convince us about a certain ability until it is done by someone else or by ourselves,* he thought, *almost as if we do not want to consider anything that isn't known to us already... That is such a limit* he added, *even more so, a limit to oneself...*

*

The watch buzzed again announcing the end of this session. With the ten-minute mark done, the boy started making his way out the lake, his body shivering and tensing with each step. He felt proud and extremely cold. Standing by the towel, he looked down at his chest and realized there is a contrasting redness covering the part of his body, which was submerged in the cold for so long. It looked like the skin was on fire. He chuckled feeling his teeth clench and clatter. Shivers all around, he wrapped himself in a towel and started changing into warmer clothing. His awareness heightened by the temperature offered a great deal of satisfaction and an avalanche of thoughts concerning the topic. He thought of the limiting beliefs he has granted himself throughout his youth, and about those that hold in place many beings around him, *how much do we disallow ourselves...?* Trying to dress up he struggled, as both, his toes and fingers didn't seem to work properly. Putting on shoes, he had to sit down, as there was little if any control over the way his hands dealt with the task. With his gaze rested at the lake, he observed his friend taking his personal best to the new height, lasting over twelve minutes inside the water. It was an early morning, plenty of time to take care of other things later in the day. It was the time for healing.

*

Driving back home with his body wrapped up warm in the many layers, the boy was listening to a speech. The thesis made by the speaker offered a glimpse of what the boy considered a few moments earlier while standing still in coldness.

137

What kind of stories and beliefs do you constrict yourself with the speaker asked the crowd, *what kind of limits did you put on you...?*

*

Letting the mind do its work, allowing the inner discussion to take the lead, he drove across the city to get back home and start the day. It was the end of the year and a perfect time to review and rewire his life.

What things am I stopping myself from doing he pondered, *which beliefs should I discard, and which should I acquire...?*

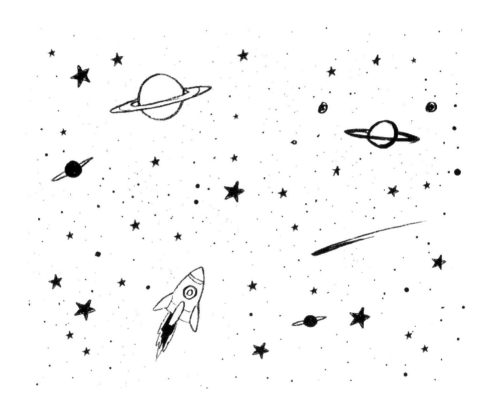

ABOUT DREAMS

Are dreams mirrors of our lively thoughts and experiences, or is our daily life the mirror of the dream-like state?

The boy walked slowly, hesitantly even, through the streets of his hometown. He looked around as he pondered on the question, that arose in his mind a few moments earlier. Glancing at different pieces of human-made architecture he noticed plants in the area, planted both with the hands of the people as well as the ones that forced by the power of nature emerged between those urban structures defiant of the order introduced by his civilization. He thought of the correlation between this state of constant change, a dance of nature, and the human species in a never-ending cycle. The thoughts of this contrasting yet so closely existing phenomenon brought him back to the question. *What if the dreams are the plants that come from nature, without the acceptance to the state of the world as dictated by us (humans) which can symbolize the daily life* he thought as he crossed the road and joined in the pedestrian stream following the alley. There was not much in his life that would be considered worthy of a dream, at least that's what the boy thought. Living the daily routines seemed mundane most of the time, offering glances into a more meaningful experience, whenever a major change in any aspect of his existence emerged. *But what if the dreams are the 'real' world* he asked smirking to himself in awe of the absurdity of the idea. Yet the absurd somehow didn't feel that unreal. The boy approached a bench situated by the entrance to the local park and sat down cross-legged, letting his body rest as he connected with his thinking mind. *Why is it that at times my dreams relate to what I've experienced and yet I find myself living some of the dreams later on* he savoured the concept and weighted the two. *What if they are both closely connected and portrayed as a closed cycle of cause and effect that are closest to the truth…?*

*

The boy looked towards the park and focused his gaze on the blackbird that ran around the grass nearby. He noticed how erratically the bird's legs move. One by one, stepping through space as if hinges were embedded in the few areas of its limbs. The boy pondered on how the bird's supposed knees bend in the opposite direction to his own. He found that quite amusing. Looking down on his own, he considered what the legs of a bird would appear in the state out of the conscious, ordinary world. *Maybe* he thought, *maybe what is here a 'normal' would be considered absurd in the world of dreams.* Imagination fuelled the wondering as he closed his eyes and focused on remembering the dream from a few nights before.

Isn't it weird how we remember the dreams he thought. Can we even say we remember them at all if we never truly experienced them, he added. What if the mind is unable to see the difference and therefore considers them true and adds to our mental library of memories the question echoed through his thoughts. Like a ripple on a pond, its novelty intrigued him, sending the mind on a roller-coaster ride alongside both abstract and very earthly ideas.

The boy opened his eyes and again glanced towards the bird. But it wasn't there. He looked around in search of a black, erratically moving creature, only to discover most of the street was empty as well. Even the pedestrians, who earlier flooded the streets were nowhere to be found. The boy felt a pinch in his stomach. His gut started its usual, troubled monologue, as he raised himself and turned around a few times. *No one, nowhere* he thought surprised by his discovery. Feeling anxious thoughts joining in the dance, he walked a few steps towards the turn of the square, hoping to find some signs of life behind it. Heart raised its speed as he approached the corner. The surprise struck his thinking mind with such a force, he stopped and took a step back in disbelief. The street was empty. He gazed on the horizon, trying to reason with what his eyes tell him to be true. There was no one, nowhere; neither human nor animal of any kind.

The boy's demeanour seemed to diminish as he arched his back and looked down under his feet. Waves of sadness, confusion, and fear washed his mind clean of any thoughts of positive nature. He stood there speechless, hopeless. *Pointless* he thought to himself. Looking back towards the park he noticed a little movement, somewhere, somehow. His heart skipped a beat; his palms sweaty, as he raised one hand to his brow and squinted his eyes looking against the sun. Lowering its body, the greatest of the flashlights obscured the parking area with a shaded cloak of the night. The boy focused the gaze with all his eyes might and took a step forward. The movement of unknown origin was gone. He took another step and slowly with erratic moves, he continued towards the bench, where he was sat in the first place. With each move forward the sun seemed to lower and give way to his walk. He kept glancing around in hope of finding some signs of life, as he approached the park entrance. *I didn't realize it is so late* he thought realizing how much darker his surroundings appeared. He sat down in the same spot, in a similar manner, and pondered on the nature of this experience he got himself in. *One moment you try to understand the nature of the unconscious and suddenly the conscious seems to doubt its own* he smiled at the irony of the situation. *Trying to understand what's outside logic I arrived at an illogical place* he exclaimed out loud accenting the discovery with a brief laugh. *Maybe I am just going insane* he thought instantly losing his smile to the sea of worries. He decided not to move and tried to approach the problem he faced with a calm attitude. *I am here* he touched the wooden surface of the bench *therefore I am.* He rested his palm on the heart area of the chest and quietened the mind. *My heart is beating therefore I am alive* he concluded. *Looking around he named a few items of what he saw. I can see therefore I am awake* he thought, but his stomach rose alarmingly to his neck, making him doubt the statement instantly. *What if I am far from awake,* he pondered and tried pinching his arm a few times. The pain of the pinch resonated through the body, yet no awakening took place. The boy felt weird as if all that he experienced resembled only a part of his true life. He considered his options and tried to remember any tricks, that might come in handy to a person stuck in what he thought was an unconscious state. He got up and started running around in circles, hoping to accelerate his heartbeat and with that awaken the body. The heart raced faster and faster, yet no major change occurred. Breathing heavily, he stopped and stood on the grassy area, where he saw the bird beforehand. His mind boggled with the nature of the situation seemed to wander more and more. He felt somehow disassociating with it more and more with each moment. The boy looked at his own hands and arrived at a wacky conclusion that neither the right nor the left hand appears to be true to itself.

He didn't recognize them. Twisting his fingers, giving them a pinch, and throwing his wrists around he tried to realize his situation. His movement became more erratic, his legs resembling those of the blackbird, suddenly as if struck with a wave of ecstasy or a flash of stormy lightning he fell to the ground. His head rested on the grass, which seemed soft in look but impossible to feel. The boy fell unconscious.

*

The evening altered the appearance of the world as the boy awakened. He felt a huge wave of pain splashing down his spine as he raised his uncomfortably slouched body to seated. He was still on the bench. He looked around in confusion, his eyes resembling the nature of the sleep. A few pedestrians walked past him immersed in their conversations. The boy glanced towards the grassy area considering what seemed to be a memory of that place. To his surprise, the bird was still there, pecking a pack of crisps on the side of the street. He noticed the erratic movement of the bird's legs and instantly flushed with a vivid vision remembered the final moments of his fall to the ground, what seemed to be a few moments ago. He smiled to himself wondering what this whole experience got him through. *It must have been a dream* he thought. He remembered the question that inspired all of the past few, what must have been hours, and considered it again.

*

What if the dreams are nothing more than interlaced, alternative, and inseparable parts of the 'real life' experience… Maybe it is not only a motor for the reality, or the reality being a motor for the dream state, but they are also one and of one for the mind. The boy thought of it strongly, considering all ideas that emerged as the sub-products of the previous concepts.

*

Maybe what makes up for our 'reality' is considered solely through the thinking mind, which in its objectivity does not judge upon the 'truthfulness' of the experience, and therefore cannot tell the difference without our awakened, conscious effort. *Would it mean that both dreams and 'real life' make up for the life itself…? Which one then, should we consider more 'real'?*

CREATING

'Imagination is more important than knowledge. Knowledge is limited. Imagination encircles the world.'

~ Albert Einstein

AGAINST THE DOUBT

When you write in belief that the words arising are not your own, but those of God himself, you can easily take the Inner Critic and chuck him out the window. After all, it's not your work anyway...

You are preaching to the wrong crowd the boy told him looking behind his shoulder. He was stood by the wall, fidgeting with his long, awfully slim hands. He didn't care to look. He never does. *All you do is criticize* he added, chucking the crumpled piece of paper at his face. He glanced at the boy, avoiding his gaze. Thinking that he must be too scared to even look him straight in the eye, he smirked and turned to face the page. *Time to write something great* he thought to himself and started typing sporadically. The speaker on the side filled the room with funky sounds of relaxing jazz, as he continued his attempt. *There is no attempt here* he contemplated *after all I am just letting the writing write itself.* The critic finally moved from the wall. The boy could feel his presence as he closed to his back and again glanced above the shoulder in search for mistakes and 'weak writing' as he called it. Over the years the boy tried everything with him. Sometimes he would write his opinions next to the sentences and let them be there in hope that, once written, they will lose their power. In other instances, he would spend the whole writing session trying to argue with his views, discussing all 'buts' and 'ifs', as if that was the work that a writer should fulfil. The boy even tried pushing him out the room or forcing to get him a cup of coffee, but all he did then was shouting his preachings a little louder through the door or preparing the most bitter coffee one could ever imagine. In other words, their relationship was one of trouble and animosity in nature. *This time* he thought*, this time it is different.* He came up with another, new solution; one that hopefully would get him to shut up without spending too much of his time trying to do so. Smiling to himself he felt the hope of success arising within. It was the time to act and being as good as any other time, he decided to take the first step. Announcing to him the belief, he lifted a few weights holding his writing down. Nevertheless, there was a lot of work still to be done. Pondering on the nature of creativity the boy recently arrived at the conclusion, that as long as the artist keeps the work to himself and actively invites the Higher Power (whatever one can call it) to co-operate with his efforts, he can disassociate his works from himself, letting the reasoning with the Inner Critic change in dynamics. *How can I argue about something that isn't mine* he thought and to his surprise, the bully seemed to somehow feel the difference, glancing above the shoulder from further away and smacking his lips less often.

Excited for the effects and happy with how the situation unfolded, the boy continued tapping away. His fingers floated above the buttons, finding their momentary place, only to fly towards the next one once the letter was secured. He thought of his palms as of the hard-working bees, which continuously buzzed around the fields of flowers, sitting down for a moment on each of those, which found their liking. The boy tried not to look behind, reminding himself that the critic came uninvited and therefore can be ignored. Every now and then, his grumpy voice would echo through the air, as he tried to undermine the wording or point out the accidental coma. The boy nodded, corrected the mistakes, and sometimes give sporadic *thanks,* whenever his advice was one of value, not caring about his views on the substance of the work. *It isn't yours, neither mine* the boy told him, grinning with satisfaction. *He seems to bother* he told himself *he is just trying to hide it between the waves of arguments and painful words.* He knew at that point that this time he won. It might not be the end of the war, but it ended today's battle, and thinking of this as an example to follow and improve on in future endeavours, the boy felt energized and motivated. He tapped out the ending sentence and looked back at the critic once more. He stood by the wall as he usually did but his demeanour seemed weaker than before. He didn't dare to look at the boy, scratching his itchy elbow in consternation. Smiling the boy stood up from his seat, taking a long, wide stretch. His yawn filled the space between them. He approached him and patted his shoulder, as he walked out of the room. *You can come back tomorrow* he said *but don't expect any better than today... I think I found a way to get you exiled* he added. The boy slammed the door behind and continued up the stairs for breakfast. He felt some weight off my shoulders was lifted as he floated above each and every step of the way.

WITH INSPIRATION

What makes a writer great…?

The boy pondered on the question, as his lower back ached for little relief. But there was no rest planned. At least not yet. Resisting the urge to get up and move around, he shuffled in his seat and tried to focus on the subject, pushing the back pain to the back. He didn't want to start again, knowing how hard it was to start writing anything in the first place. *It seems a bit dull at times* he thought, reflecting on his recent writings and mornings spent in a half-bent position, over the notebook and laptop, which seemed to be his only companions, on the journey to literacy salvation, without who he wouldn't be able to write so diligently, day by day. *I don't mean that they write it for me* he stated *only that their presence, their existence, has a huge deal of influence and pressure within them, which manifests in my life, whenever my attempt to write anything emerges. It is easier to make yourself suffer if there is something to write that suffering on, rather than if you could only say it out loud… I know exclaiming certain sentences might help with their emotional baggage and value, but the essence about writing comes from the writer himself, spending days on end, writing, re-writing, editing, thinking, sipping hot drinks, and occasionally going for a walk, to give the mind a break. None of these things made it easier to write, only made it what it is – a struggle with the most demanding enemy of all – ourselves.* He observed his hands, as their palms floated above the keyboard, spontaneously choosing the letter of their fancy, and quickly traversing their course to yet another, and another and another. Click, click, click, click… Click. Each letter emerges from the abyss of emptiness and soon enough connects with others, in constant dance towards a perfect sentence, verse, or paragraph. Not knowing still, what is that makes the writer 'great', the boy looked towards the bookshelf and analysed all possible inspirations, that seemed to 'make it' onto the shelf, and therefore could be considered, at least partially successful as their writing became contemporary, and made its way onto a shelf of such an ordinary fellow he was. He read the covers, scanning through memories of high school literature education, A-Levels, and a brief creative writing module done in the third year of his undergraduate degree. Shakespeare, Dostoevsky, Christie… Murakami. Some were more contemporary; some had a distinctive motif or style. All seemed to be considered good entertainment at the least, and a greatly valuable and insightful knowledge source at best. He pondered on the style, trying to find a certain pattern of thoughts, emotional inputs, or simply the use of certain words over the other.

None of his work seemed to particularly express this doubtful 'originality'. The boy thought of the word-formation, sentence flow, tempo, rhythm, and all other aspects of writing, as it can be, struggling to find anything, that would catch the eye for longer than a brief confusion of time. *There is nothing special about my writing* he heard his thoughts, whose inspiration drawn undoubtedly from the 'inner critic', whose works never made it to the page, but who always seems to have something 'important' to say. He thought of the interactions between him and that voice over the past few months. Since he started dedicating each morning to writing, the voice seemed to give me space more often, coming back to the room, again and again, only to discover there is not much he can criticize about the creative attempts and therefore quickly withdrawing back outside. *He doesn't like my work, but he hates my working even more* he concluded, seeing the back of the critic disappearing behind the door, as the next sentence arrived on the page. Thinking of all the times, his writing was postponed due to the simple fact, that the inner critic was too loud to bear. *Never again* he acclaimed, clenching his fist involuntarily, remembering all these times when nothing at all came to life from writing, simply because he (the inner critic) was too overwhelming for the mind to deal with. Reminiscing on these failures and lack of attempts, back in the day, the boy pondered whether any of the authors, who he so joyfully read, had the same problem at any time in their career. *I cannot be the only one* he thought. Trying to recognize whether he was in the right, he called one of his friends, whose writing always seems to uplift his spirit and make the heart dance a wholehearted swing, similarly to the writer's swinging emotional imbalance connected to the failure of these writing attempts. *Do you think Shakespeare had troubles with writing* he asked, listening in to the phone, trying to expect the unexpected, but to tell the truth, already expecting the outcome, as his friend's words followed. *I don't think anyone doesn't have them* she said, and with saying their goodbyes, they disconnected. He sat back down, his emotions simmering on the side of the chair, where the butt met the surface, leaving his body in a subtle shake of relief and excitement. *If everyone has troubles writing, then why wouldn't they just stop* he asked himself, feeling the urge to write down what he has concluded. The boy reached out to the laptop and opened a new text document. Leaving his critic alone, he started writing, letting the fingers do their magic, as his mind pondered. *I don't know what makes a great writer* he noted but *I know what makes a writer in the first place.*

THROUGH ASPIRATION

The difference between aspiration and achievement is the doing…

There was a fiery flame within the boy whenever he would lay his hands on the keyboard of his laptop or when the tip of the pen would initiate the first scribble of the words yet to be evoked. He wanted to become a writer. His wish to create, describe, notice, and commemorate was his passion and the deepest of the desires held in the heart for as long as he could remember. He didn't always know this. There was a time he felt like he needed to sing, for some time he drew and painted, he wanted to make movies, to write poems, and to describe great books and stories to people all around him. Only recently, in the last few years, the drive to create in the realm of writing became apparent enough for his mind to stop finding other ways to let this creative steam off. His brief sensation of bliss, which came whenever his hands flowed down the lines on paper; the pen being the extension of his soul, made him realize the need and want to be who the writing ascribed itself to. Once this realization came, the shift in himself became apparent and quickly strengthened his will to do what's necessary to attain the career his heart so strongly longed for. He read books without a break, he studied the writers before him, he subscribed to articles, newsletters, and information forums, which seemed to step away from the same branch of the industry he so strongly wanted to become accustomed to. There wasn't a day when his wish to create wouldn't express itself one way or another. He wrote poems, stories, essays, tiny sentences filled with beautiful words, and thought of the possible opportunities out there to express himself and to show off that, which simmered on the hob of his heart. The one question hanging on his back like a heavy stone, which weights the person down once their body and the entangled rope with the weight hits the surface of the deep seas – *when does one become a writer…?*

*

They say a director can call themselves that once they have directed a play; a singer becomes a singer once their song has been heard; an architect can call themselves one once the building they envisioned becomes a reality… *When does a writer become one,* he pondered, sat at his little desk made of a chipped, mashed together woodblock, which resembled the wooden pallets recognizable from afar for their industrial outlook. *Can I call myself one when a book with my name on it is published,* he wondered, *maybe there needs to be a review of it to make it viable…?* Hesitant of answers, his heart suffered, lack of self-assurance being the reason for the pain.

He worked on his craft, kept writing without a stop, agitated sometimes drowned with sorrows, he continued coming back to the page, again and again, listening to the inner voice, which seemed to be more and more of help as his practice continued. He truly felt like a writer already, yet because of all the title-calling and bracketing, which took place in the society, he wanted to know for sure. He longed for the unattainable, for the assurance that what he is doing does count as a writer's job. *What for* - one day a question sprung to his mind, *what for do I need this reassurance...? What difference does it make* he exclaimed, letting the neighbour hear his late-night outrage, *isn't the writing in itself enough to state this...?* His ego seemed to oppose, coming up with all the excuses and reasons for the difficulty of this dilemma, yet he felt the different opinion rising above all within his heart. He felt that the writing is enough already. He felt he was a writer long before he even decided to become one. *What does a writer do* he asked the space confined within the four walls of his flat. Silence and a distant noise of the street answered. He looked around the room, which filled with his personal belongings drew a little story of itself. His face grinned into a smile, as he asked a question again, feeling a little stupid yet much energized to do so, *what does a writer do?!* A moment of quiet satisfaction prevailed. He picked up a piece of paper and took a marker from the pile of pencils and drawing equipment, which covered the corner of his writing-table. *A writer writes* he scribbled across the page, making the letters thick and visible, squeezing the marker between his fingers, his knuckles going white from the pressure he has put into it. *That is what a writer does* he exclaimed pointing the tip of the pen at the written sentence and smiling towards his reflection in the window he raised the paper in triumph, *a writer writes... That is what a writer does.* He found a piece of blue tac within his box of random office articles and stuck the little ball into the wall across the room, right above the place he would eat his breakfast at. Slamming the paper against the sticker he let the sentence hang above his eating area. *The only difference between aspiration and achievement is the doing* he recited a sentence that has been on his mind for quite a while, *a writer writes, therefore I am a writer already...*

*

Screams of joy and satisfaction echoed through the street as the boy sat down to his laptop and decided to slam out a few more paragraphs of private mumbling, which maybe, just maybe, would one day become apparent to someone outside his house.

The writing flowed effortlessly, as he scribbled his thoughts on the pages, taking short breaks to appreciate the feeling the writing gave him, astounded with the fact and simplicity of it – *I am a writer already, whenever I put my pen to paper… it's so simple!*

REGARDLESS THE STRUGGLE

I.   *Sometimes the best you can do is just do what's yours to be done, regardless of the pervasive feeling of lack…*

The boy was sat in front of a blank page, squeezing his worn-out pen between his lean fingers. Fidgeting without a stop, he struggled for words to even start the page with. *It's just one of those days* his mind expressed its opinion, *maybe just let it go for a bit…* He frowned at the attitude residing within him and biting the tip of the pen, he waited. The day has just begun and as everyone in his household was still fast asleep, he felt satisfied with his situation, regardless of the lacking inspiration, which seemed to be the case. He was proud to be here, no matter what the outcome would turn out to be. *I bet everyone sometimes struggles for words* he pondered, trying to uplift his spirit with a little comparison, *even a hen doesn't bring an egg every day…* Smiling at this rather silly idea he felt that there is something true about it, as he couldn't imagine an egg being brought to reality from the hen's insides every day. *That would be a bit too much wouldn't it,* he mumbled to himself and laughed briefly at the sound of his encouraging statement, *so I am like a hen now huh?* Scribbling a little note to himself for later he noted to check how often does an average hen brings eggs and looking down at the piece of paper again he struggled to keep his cool without chuckling. Pondering on what to write, the boy sat there without a little clue of what should be done in this situation. *Maybe I should try to do some other things before coming back to writing* he considered his options, *a walk for the start, or a meditation of some sort…* Ideas flew in and out of his head without stopping, yet none seemed to match any constructive creativity, he was used to seeing manifest itself within his mind. *Bollocks,* he mumbled quietly and got up to make himself a cup of coffee, realizing he hasn't had one and maybe, just maybe, that is what his rusty mind of the day needed to keep itself a bit more upbeat for this miserable writing block. Grinning to himself in the realization of what he is expecting of a simple cup of coffee, he prepared the drink gazing out to the world through the window of his kitchen. *What about the sun* the question echoed in his mind, *does the sun have days like this..?*

Coffee made, honey sweetening the bitter taste of the dark essence, he sat down to his paper once more, hoping to find 'the right words' for the page. *Certainly, the sun doesn't have these days of lack* he pondered squeezing the warm cup between his palms, *and even if it does, it surely does not go back to its bed thinking 'oh well, better luck tomorrow'*... Chuckling a little, he wrote down his thought of the sun going back to bed on a day such as this one and realized that this might be a great explanation - maybe a little abstract, for what makes the days rainy or cloudy. *Maybe* he thought, *the sun is the main star of the play but once it's feeling a bit iffy, someone else has to take over...* He laughed a little noting down his idea, *maybe the clouds and the rain are nothing more than distractive extras in the production, needed for the sun to take a little break once in a while!* His last words sounded loud, too loud. Covering his mouth with his hand, he grinned in amusement, realizing that this little concept has gotten him a bit too excited. *I bet it must be difficult to work with such a star like a sun* he pondered letting the hand note every little idea that surfaced to the top of the mind's ocean.

The gears of his imagination have warmed up, oiled with the little laughter and morning coffee, which as bitter as it was, gave him a little pleasure to crutch on, while the initial suffering of insufficient ideas has prevailed. He considered the possible reasons why such a star like a sun could be excluded from coming to work and realized that the list is not the lengthiest one, making him think of how lucky he is with his employment regulations. *Feeling sick, depressed, or under the weather overall* he listed, *is there anything else that can exclude the sun? What about a family issue to deal with* he pondered, *surely the sun doesn't have a family being as busy as it is...* The ideas varied from those completely out of the blue to the kind of ones that everyone could encounter in a usual daily newspaper, most of them very human at the core of its struggle. *But since the sun is always there when the clouds of the storm are out and about, maybe it turns up to work every day* he pondered, *just asking for a little distraction and assistance occasionally... Maybe all the sun needs in those days is a little empathy...* Now, writing seemed seamless, almost automatic as the boy sprinted the pen across the page, noting down all that has echoed through his mind at the time, letting the inspiration sleep, while the true instant creation was at work. Smiling to himself he sipped the coffee in-between the written lines and concluded his little piece with a small quote, which seemed to fit both the sun, the hen, and his situation when considering the days such as this one. *Not every day our effort might work, but every day the work needs some effort, however small* he moved his lips silently, as the words were noted on the page, *there are no times off in life so why would one get a day off from the life he works for...*

II.   *There are days, when your mind feels blank, like a piece of paper that flew away in the wind, losing a chance of becoming a part of someone's great work...*

The boy was sat at his flat, which smelled of the laundry wash and damp. He had to do the laundry and after taking it back home, he realized that it didn't dry off completely, leaving him with the option of hanging the clothes all around his house or taking it back to the laundrette. The choice was his. Out of laziness, or maybe discouraged by the efficiency of the dryers provided in the public laundrette, he took it all back and used all possible hanging spaces to let it dry off a little more. Sitting on his bed, his legs straightened and spread across the folds of made bedding, he opened his laptop and decided to finally do the day's writing. How big was his surprise, as in the usual subject-choosing moment, he didn't feel like describing anything specifically *what am I to write about* he pondered. He looked out the window, which offered a rather poor vision of the outside world. A big, metal pipe, corroded to its bones overwhelmed the view. The back of the house he chose for this year's residence was like many British homes, rather awful. Plenty of bushes, forgotten by the world, and lack of any garden space made the behind resemble the bottom of an abandoned well. The images from Pripyat came to his mind, reminding him that it could look much worse than it does. He turned to his screen again and typed in a few words, which felt encouraging but far from desirable, when one does sit down to create something beautiful *there are days...* His palms refused to continue summoning the sentence, which already appeared like a scam and his body must have recognized it. *Of course, there are days* he murmured and pressed 'delete' sending the word count down to zero, *what a day...*

*

He rested his hands on the soft, comforting surface of a blanket, which covered his bedding, and sliding his fingers up and down he tried to squeeze the mind a little. *You got to give me something* he frowned hearing the voice inside. His practice of writing was like any other practice full of ups and downs, and he seldom bothered about either. His understanding of the idea that no matter what it is one attempt, there will be both types of experiences, with a statistical advantage of those sometimes called 'negative', made him look beyond the exercise itself. It was a journey. One that does not finish until the creator is either dead or defeated by the ever-present doubt. The boy knew he isn't dead yet.

After all, he was here and quite frankly felt rather healthy and in good state of mind, therefore the only true obstacle resisting his creation could be that of defeat, meaning lack of further pursuit; and he consciously refrained from succumbing to its power. He typed a little sentence, reminding himself why in the first place did he ever picked up the idea of writing anything, *write because you love it.* The word count jumped to five, giving him a simple pleasure. He chuckled realizing how much his expectations of the daily routine dawn on him at times, *it's okay to not make it till a thousand each day you know* he said to himself out loud. Shaking his head, he got up from the bed and leaving his laptop; typing icon constantly pulsating at the end of the last written word, he walked into the kitchen and poured himself a glass of orange juice. Drinking it in one go, he felt the refreshing substance dripping down his throat, landing in the stomach. Standing in the kitchen, the glass empty squeezed between his fingers, he realized just how blank his mind feels today. *If anything, it's kind of soothing* he thought, *don't think I paid as much attention to drinking anything before…*

*

He rushed back to the bedroom, jumped landing next to his computer, and grinning into its white screen, he typed a little sentence right next to the previously written words, *but let your mind rest sometimes.* His face, brightened by the release of the guilt, which he has previously felt; its itchiness scratching the back of his mind, smiled at the device, which longed for his creative touch, yet couldn't get it this day. *I think I'm going to go for a walk* he exclaimed and proud of the feeling that has released his consciousness from the pressure of his dreams, he gave himself an approval of taking a day off. *Maybe not a day* his mind hesitated, *just a few hours* it bargained. He smirked hearing the inner dialogue and nodding his head, he took a coat and marched out the door, *maybe a few hours… We'll see and for now, just chillout…*

FOLLOWING THE IDEA

Sometimes an idea, like a brew, needs to boil and simmer for a while in the teapot of time before it does become what its potential allows it to be...

The boy had an idea in his mind for quite a while. He didn't want to share it with his friends or parents before its vision wasn't clear enough for him to express it. *It's hard sometimes to see it in the bigger picture* he reminded himself. His wish was to create a piece of writing longer than ever before. He has done scripts in the past, that was true, but there was never a time when a book of his doing came to existence and having this little nudge of a concept in his head, he went about his days doing all he could to aim his creative insight towards this goal. He liked writing short stories and essays, he enjoyed it thoroughly. Yet something was missing from them, that didn't let him sleep calmly at night. He felt like he needed to write a bigger piece as if that format were to be considered proof that he truly is 'a writer' already. *I guess I am one already* he would agree sometimes, talking to his friend or a family member, *but I feel like there is more and I want to discover it...* They would nod their heads, smile empathetically, and sometimes even grant a little encouragement but their perception of his state was far from the truthful one. It could appear to some that his writing was causing him suffering rather than providing a way to express his true Self, but this happens sometimes when those who observe us cannot relate to the activity or passion, we are engaging in. The boy didn't mind it, it was his for the making and the taking and he knew that one way or another it will be as his wishes expected.

*

Water boiled and the boy got up from his seat to finish preparing himself his morning coffee. His ritual was pretty much identical for each day, time sometimes being the only difference. Once he was about to start writing there was either already a cup of coffee made, waiting by his side or the water was about to boil in the kitchen, ready to be used for making one. He liked these little rituals as they felt helpful in settling himself into the 'zone' of writing he so highly valued. A few special words of encouragement he wrote for himself welcomed him every time his laptop would 'wake up' and as he wrote his first line of the piece, he always remembered to invite the Universe to help him in being creative that morning. *It's the little things that matter* he would claim, whenever someone pointed out his somewhat weird or eccentric habits. He brought the cup back to the desk and smelled the great aroma hanging above the surface of the dark-brown liquid. There was a slight note of honey as he preferred his drink with this naturally sourced sweetener.

It makes it taste like the home he would say, recollecting his childhood, when honey was the thing added to both teas and coffees as well as on top of the oatmeal or cereal, *it's healthier too* he would repeat his mother's phrase. The idea within was still warming up, his mind working like a hob on full power, ready to overflow the pot as the steamy, hot liquid of creativity would begin to boil. *It takes time,* he murmured, writing down a sentence that just came to his mind, *no worries, we've got time...* He smiled to his reflection in the window in front of him, the world outside still quite dark as the early hour of the day just sent the invite for the sun to arrive.

*

His everyday work was different, every time a little more or less interesting to him, every time subtly touching on a topic close to his heart, yet very often not much thought about. *It's amazing how much more my writing can express in comparison to the potential discussion I would have on the same topic* he thought, *it's almost like when writing happens it is not me who writes it...* He liked that idea, as he felt like there is always a way to excuse a bad piece as well as the humility to not get carried away by the good one, as it was not him who wrote it in the first place. *It's convenient,* he concluded. Looking at the clock, he realized that there are only ten minutes left until his work starts. Saving the project and putting the laptop into the bag, he rushed around the flat collecting necessary items and run out the door exactly seven minutes to the hour. *I won't be late if I run,* he thought, *thankfully the ideas can simmer on our minds regardless of the space we are in...*

OUT OF LOVE

Isn't playing the guitar, similarly to any other skilled art, lovemaking at its best?

The boy pondered on the question as he watched a street musician's fingers dancing on the threats of the guitar. The music resonated throughout the public space, which filled with crowds of tourists, locals and in-betweeners flowed down the avenue. The boy was sat on the stone wall nearby a small flowerbed, waiting for his bus home. His backpack and suitcase by his side, his hands resting on the worn-out notebook, that participated in most of the boys' adventures, he sat cross-legged with his head high, as if an invisible string held it so. *I can sit straight thanks to the hours of training and patience surrendered to the skill of muscle stretching* he thought. He saw an analogy between all he ever practiced and the practice of guitar, which the musician was living proof of. Amazed with the sounds, rhythm, and the tempo of the entertainment, served by that, slightly older than him, street performer, he opened his notebook on a new, blank page and wrote down the date in the corner, making sure to check, which day it is. *What a weird time to experience, when each day seems so similar to another, that one needs to check the date before writing it down,* he announced in his mind, and looking up at the crowd, observed the situation he felt lucky to participate in. His dreams conveyed a story of a writer, who with all his hard work, long hours of practice, multiple shortcomings, and many adventures to put into writing strove to become one of the greats and join the respected panel of pen warriors. He looked up to those who in different times and spaces, made their works to entertain, amaze, inspire, and provoke readers all over the globe. Whenever he wrote, he felt this exquisite intimacy within. Whenever the pen met the paper, whenever his palms stroked the keyboard in the prayer for creation, he felt as if all around him disappeared behind a transparent veil of focus and attention. *That's what being in the zone feels like* he thought, considering the focus written on the face of the man, who played so beautifully asking the people around him for a moment of attention and a spare change to get through the next day. He thought of the question, that arose so naturally, so subtly at the back of his vast mind, when he sat down to hear the performance. The boy already experienced love. He was not sure if there is any right definition of love, as all his encounters were different in many ways, but similar in one pure aspect of comfort and hope that experiencing this emotion brought.

He thought of the times when his palms met the skin of a loved, praised body of his date, in the same way as in times of writing, letting the mind wander as all the consciousness attention was aimed at experiencing what one has been allowed to. In those brief moments of joy, the levels of his admiration for the world flowed gently above the surface of time and space, looking beyond what's to be heard or seen. He pondered on the pleasures that both of these sensations brought, while their bodies intertwined in a sensual dance, twirled and turned inside out, offering a glimpse into the eternity, which during the majority of ones' life seemed so distant and unreachable. *Practice makes perfect but perfect does not need to attend any practices* the boy savoured his thought and writing down a few sentences on the page, glimpsed at the station, which took up space in front of a large monument. The boy could not see what the monument was founded for but the statue of the horseman, which boasted its beauty on top of the concrete block, offered an intuitional feel of success and achievement, which the landmark promoted. Or at least that is what the boy thought at the time. The musician finished a song, and a wave of appraisal filled the street. The crowd consisted of families, people of more knowledgeable age, and a few local salesmen who offered their products served from the wheeled around baskets and carts. The man stood up from his guitar case, which served him as the seat, and bowed to the audience. A few people including the excited children started for the hat, which clanked with coins as the prize for the performance was served. The man thanked the gathered witnesses and sat down to play another piece. The boy observed them thinking if there is any spare coin in his pocket, assuming that it is rather unlikely. He picked up his backpack and opened one of the side pockets, his hand diving inside in search of pieces of conceptual value. Palms felt the touch of pencils, few written notes, a beer bottle cap, and something round, that sent the thought of hope into his mind. He took out the assumed coin and opened his hand encountering a foreign to his place of stay currency. He smiled realizing the humour of the situation and pondered momentarily on the idea of giving this to the musician regardless of its unfitting origin. *It is money isn't it,* he reasoned with himself, putting away the backpack and shuffling in his seat. He decided to 'go with the flow' of the events and hid the coin in his pocket as the musician started his second song. The crowd murmur quietened, and the street seemed to surrender to the artists' performance, as it felt calmer than a moment ago. The boy observed the show as the man struck the strings, filling the space with melodies, which appeared to stand above the crowd, like the horseman on the pedestal.

The cascades of sounds flew around the square, reaching the facades of the buildings, fences, and windows, breaking through the hearts and minds of all that were in the vicinity to experience it. The melody was soft and subtle yet sharp and strong, the rhythm changing in constant balance between the frequencies of waves. The boy felt like the song is pumping energy into the surrounding area. He could almost see it happen. The crowd waved side to side, some people clapped along, the kids danced around their parents' legs, the dog lied down by someone's feet. The boy felt the power of music and sitting cross-legged, accompanied by his belongings, in this strange to him space sensed the comfort of acceptance and unity. *That is the beauty of art* he observed, thinking of all the times people enjoy the efforts of others, letting themselves be fully present in the moment. The audience in a theatre that gasp at each move of the actor, the spectators in the cinema whose eyes follow the directors' vision, the reader whose heart races when the protagonist is about to uncover the terrifying truth and like in any other work or act, the participators are given a chance to fill their souls with something that comes from a further realm. The boy thought how similar this experience is to a sunset, which promotes stillness in the wait for what happens every day for millennia to amaze the viewer yet again. Always exquisite, always different, always the same. Drifting in the ocean of time (past, present, and future), which for each life unfolds simultaneously and separately in every moment, is only experienced in the now, offers a unifying space of awe and community. The boy his heart dance. His spirit lifted with each played chord, he gazed at the scene, which became his companion in the wait for the means to come home. His bus was planned to leave in fifteen minutes and as he looked at the watch again, he realized that the time does fly sometimes. His time was almost up, his body twitched with an uneasy feeling of potential lateness. He got up and grabbed his belongings, his ears still focused on the beautiful melody written in the air of sounds. He walked towards the performance, thinking of the coin he was about to grant the man, as the song came to an end. The crowd applauded once more, offering a wave of happiness that stroke the hearts of the present and the boy joined a few people that approached the hat with their change. The man stood up again and bowed smiling in humility, he approached the hat as the boy was about to drop his coin in. *Thank you* he said picking up the hat and reaching it out to the boy, as he stopped and smiled. *Thank you for your art* the boy said and pointing at his coin he added *this one isn't from here, but I couldn't find any other.* The man smiled wider and nodded slightly *all the coins like all the art is worth the same, no matter the signature, it's what it represents that counts.* The boy smiled with his eyes and sharing this beautiful moment, dropped the piece into the man's hat.

Well said affirmed the boy and thanked the man leaving for the bus. The commotion settled once more, as the musician took his earnings, chucked into his guitar case, and sat back down for another song. The boy walked off feeling blissful, savouring the words of the artist. *That is a beautiful way to put it* he thought of his words. He thought of the idea that initiated this powerful experience. He thought of all the similarities that in his opinion narrowed the gap between each of the experiences. Art – written, sung, or painted, love – spoken, acclaimed, or felt, appraisal – experienced, given or granted with a prize.

All those things that bring us closer to one another and to this higher state, which flows above us at any given time, but only through pure focus and acceptance can be experienced, were infallibly the reason for a life worth living he thought.

FOR ART

Wishing for things sometimes reminds me of kicking a little rock towards a pond. On one hand, you are certain it will ultimately sink in the water, on the other you do not know what can be found underneath…

The boy was walking through the forest. His feet bare for no apparent reason, clamped against the ground with a mist of dust swirling around them, as he went through the woods during one of those hot, dangerously dry summer days. The sun beamed between the leaves, reaching his shoulders now and then with a warm, slightly too warm sensation of presence, which the boy seemed to enjoy sporadically. Carrying his shoe pair, which dangled around his right knee, he made his way down the path without giving much thought to the direction in which he was heading. Lost in his thoughts he continued the walk, keeping a fast, hard to name as a 'leisurely', pace. His mind was present but only in the sense of space, rather than time, as his wishes, which he was so intensively considering, kept its dimensional presence away from the current situation. The boy was wishing for his dream to come true and in that wish, he was immersed, like only a person of true affection towards a certain thing, activity or another being can be. The gears of his thinking machinery turned and squeaked silently, as he considered all possible solutions and approaches as to what it is one should make to fulfil ones' desire. Keeping the pace in a way, that could suggest a mechanical approach to the idea of a walk, the boy entered a clearing and stopped for a moment, realizing the sun is intrusively scorching his whole demeanour.

*

He looked around, taken out of the state of inner thought, and noticed where his pointless walk has taken him. The clearing consisted of a few fallen trees, a bunch of bushes on the side, and a little pond, which to the boy's amazement was still full of water. Considering the drought and overall climate changes, which presently affected his part of the globe, he was surprised to see any source of life-giving liquid around these areas. Leaving the subject of his wishes for a moment, he approached the bristling surface of the pond, looking down upon his reflection within. The surface shimmered reflecting all that has surrounded him as well as the sky above, so clear as if there was never a cloud present in the world. Feeling joy upon the discovery, he decided to stay here for a moment, and dipping his hands on the bright surface, he turned around to find one of the nearby trees underneath which he sat down, letting his body rest, as his mind continued the wonderful wander.

Time passed as the sun moved in the sky, or maybe the sky moved around the sun, as the boy sat there considering his future, past and present, leaning his body on the trunk of the half-fallen tree. Hidden in the shade, he was not bothered by the overwhelming warmth of the day. His shoes rested loosely next to his person, reminding him of a forgotten artifact of some kind, ready to be discovered and put into use, once again regaining their qualities and special powers. Sitting with his hands behind his head, he gazed softly towards the pond, thinking of all the opportunities that the upcoming year of his life had to offer, deciding what it is he should be focusing his efforts upon and where should he look for the wished results, for he wanted to become a writer. The dream might not seem so impossible for anyone these days, with all the technology and approachable opportunities to work on one's craft, but the boy was thinking of it on a different note.

*

He looked towards the pond, which reflected the sky's and sun's brightness around, and considered himself as the pond, in which the reflection of the world can be found. The boy thought of the idea, that whatever one experiences, one must consider for oneself, therefore making it his own. This experiential approach or understanding of the world could, in his opinion, be of great use to a prominent writer, which he considered himself to be, the only issue being, he didn't know if he was any good. Even more so, who would want to read his writing anyway... He shed a tear considering his highest dreams being those of the written glory, and looking towards the sky, he got up putting his hands behind his back. Leaning slightly forward he took a few steps towards the pond and encountering a little rock on the ground, without thinking, kicked it towards the water. The stone bounced off the ground a few times and sunk in the shimmering surface, leaving only a parade of circles to echo throughout the pond. The wish has been made, recited, and reminded so many times, now it was time for action...

THE END

EPILOGUE

Thank you for giving your precious time to my thoughts conveyed in this book.

As long as there was one thing, even the smallest one, you found between the lines of these pages, that will support your life journey, I have achieved my goal.

In the end, I wanted to offer you this piece of writing…

Our planet is but a speck of dust in the grandiose of the Universe.
Each of us but a grain of sand in the vast dunes of Sahara.
Our life but a momentary whisper in the endless echo of the Big Bang.
To understand this contrast is
to set oneself free from the shackles of worry.
We, who are marching to the beats of our hearts,
should remember just this
to keep marching,
keep going,
keep trying.
We, who are here for just a moment can choose
to make the moment worthwhile.
Regardless of the circumstances.

I wish you all the best and will see you in this life or the next.

Sincerely,
Wojciech Salski

ABOUT THE AUTHOR

For as long as I can remember I have been telling stories. Some were more interesting than others, some fitted the situation, and some did not. Learning about myself, soon enough I have decided to pursue a career within the realm of my passion for storytelling.

I write, film, and record, making the necessary mistakes and 'quantum leaps' along the way. Philosophy and art have been the biggest inspiration for most, if not all of my works.
I believe that each of us has many great stories to tell and I think it is our mission to do so.

That is why, through storytelling, I am trying to make the world a better place, one word at a time…

If you have enjoyed this book and would like to explore more of my works, you can find them on my website:
www.wsalski.com
You can also reach out to me by sending an email to: contact@salski.pl

If you have enjoyed the illustrations do not forget to see other works by Katarzyna Druszcz on her portfolio!

Printed in Great Britain
by Amazon